CLASSIC

# MIND
# BENDERS

# MIND
# BENDERS

By Terry Stickels

**Main Street**
A division of Sterling Publishing Co., Inc.
New York

**Library of Congress Cataloging-in-Publication Data Available**

10  9  8  7  6  5  4  3  2  1

Published by Sterling Publishing Co., Inc.
387 Park Avenue South, New York, NY 10016
© 2005 by Sterling Publishing Co., Inc.

Material in this collection adapted from:
*Cunning Mind-Bending Puzzles*, © 2002 by Terry Stickels
*Devious Mind-Bending Puzzles*, © 2002 by Terry Stickels
*Mesmerizing Mind-Bending Puzzles*, © 2002 by Terry Stickels

Distributed in Canada by Sterling Publishing
℅ Canadian Manda Group, 165 Dufferin Street
Toronto, Ontario, Canada M6K 3H6
Distributed in Great Britain by Chrysalis Books Group PLC
The Chrysalis Building, Bramley Road, London W10 6SP, England
Distributed in Australia by Capricorn Link (Australia) Pty. Ltd.
P.O. Box 704, Windsor, NSW 2756, Australia

*Printed in China*

Sterling ISBN 1-4027-2359-8

# CLASSIC
# MIND BENDERS

## CONTENTS

**Introduction** . . . . . . . . . . . 7

**Puzzles** . . . . . . . . . . . 9

**Solutions** . . . . . . . . . . . 195

**Index** . . . . . . . . . . . 285

# INTRODUCTION

*Classic Mind Benders* has one sole purpose: for you to have fun. These brainteasers are designed so they may be solved many different ways. So please don't think there's only one way to solve them. I'll give you the way I solved them in the answer section, but your way may be just as valid.

You'll find word games, math brainteasers, spatial/ visual puzzles, and other mind treats, giving you diversity while you stretch your mind and increase your mental flexibility. If you've had a semester of algebra, you'll find it useful in solving some of the puzzles, but don't worry if you haven't … it's not mandatory. I've tried my best to create puzzles for the beginner as well as the advanced puzzle solver.

There's no time limit for any of these puzzles. Take as long as you like or skip to another puzzle and come back later to the one that has you stumped. You'll be amazed how quickly your mind starts piecing things together—and then you'll find the fun I've been discussing.

Good luck and happy puzzling!

# PUZZLES

## ✦ 1 ✦

Using only four numerals and any mathematical symbols you choose, can you produce an equation that will yield the number 300?

## ✦ 2 ✦

Suppose all counting numbers were arranged in columns as shown below. Under what letter would the number 100 appear?

| A | B | C | D | E | F | G |
|---|---|---|---|---|---|---|
| 1 | 2 | 3 | 4 | 5 | 6 | 7 |
| 8 | 9 | 10 | 11 | 12 | 13 | 14 |
| 15 | 16 | 17 | — | — | — | — |

## ✦ 3 ✦

Nancy and Audrey set out to cover a certain distance by foot. Nancy walks half the distance and runs half the distance, but Audrey walks half the time and runs half the time. Nancy and Audrey walk and run at the same rate. Who will reach the destination first (or will it be a tie)?

## ✦ 4 ✦

The following seven numbers share a unique property. What is it?

**1961 6889 6119 8008 8118 6699 6009**

## ✦ 5 ✦

Find the hidden phrase or title.

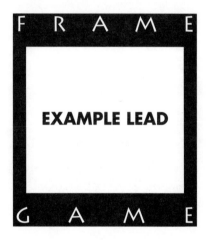

## ✦ 6 ✦

In the puzzle below, the numbers in the second row are determined by the relationships of the numbers in the first row. Likewise, the numbers in the third row are determined by the relationships of the numbers in the second row. Can you determine the relationships and find the missing number?

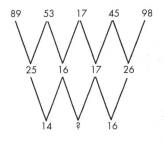

## ✦ 7 ✦

A mathematician's will stated that his wife should get one-third of his estate, his son one-fifth, his older daughter one-sixth, and his younger daughter $9,000. Who received more, his older daughter or his younger daughter?

### ✦ 8 ✦

What single-digit number should go in the box with the question mark?

| 6 | 5 | 9 | 2 | 7 |
|---|---|---|---|---|
| 1 | 4 | 3 | 5 | ? |
| 8 | 0 | 2 | 8 | 1 |

### ✦ 9 ✦

In a store that sells clocks, I notice that most of them show different times. A grandfather clock reads 2:15, an alarm clock reads 2:35, a digital clock reads 2:00, and the store clock reads 2:23. The store clerk says that a clock in the corner has just been set correctly. It reads 2:17. What is the average number of minutes, fast or slow, that these five clocks are off?

### ✦ 10 ✦

Find the missing number in the following series:

$$\frac{2}{3} \quad \frac{7}{12} \quad \frac{1}{2} \quad \frac{5}{12} \quad \frac{1}{3} \quad \frac{1}{4} \quad \frac{1}{6} \quad ?$$

### ✦ 11 ✦

Find the hidden phrase or title.

### ✦ 12 ✦

While reading a newspaper you notice that four pages of one section are missing. One of the missing pages is page 5. The back page of this section is page 24. What are the other three missing pages?

### ✦ 13 ✦

Suppose *a*, *b*, and *c* represent three positive whole numbers. If *a* + *b* = 13, *b* + *c* = 22, and *a* + *c* = 19, what is the value of *c*?

## ✦ 14 ✦

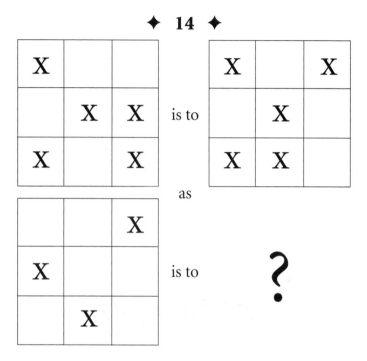

is to

as

is to

?

## ✦ 15 ✦

Below is a "trickle-down" word game. Change one letter and one letter only on each line to arrive at the word on the last line:

**MOVE**

———

———

**BARK**

## ✦ 16 ✦

Sarah is older than Julie and Maggie. Maggie is older than Paula. Ann is younger than Julie, but older than Paula. Ann is younger than Maggie. Sarah is younger than Liz. Who is the second oldest woman in this group?

## ✦ 17 ✦

What is the missing number in the following series?

**13   7   18   10   5   ?   9   1   12   6**

## ✦ 18 ✦

Find the hidden phrase or title.

## ✦ 19 ✦

How many triangles of any size are in the figure below?

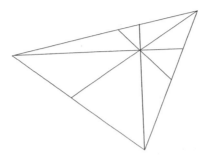

## ✦ 20 ✦

Find the hidden phrase or title.

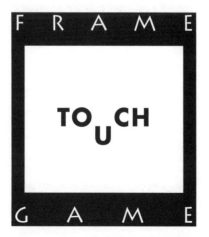

## ✦ 21 ✦

Which is larger: $2^{73}$ or $2^{70} + 2^3$ ?

## ✦ 22 ✦

Which of the following is the smallest?

a. $\dfrac{\sqrt{10}}{10}$    b. $\dfrac{1}{10}$    c. $\sqrt{10}$

d. $\dfrac{1}{\sqrt{10}}$    e. $\dfrac{1}{10\sqrt{10}}$

## ✦ 23 ✦

Find the hidden phrase or title.

## ✦ 24 ✦

There are four colored pencils—two blue, one green, and one yellow. If you took two pencils from a drawer and you knew that one was blue, what would be the likelihood that the other pencil was also blue?

## ✦ 25 ✦

Unscramble this word: **KISDTYCRA**

## ✦ 26 ✦

A certain blend of grass seed is made by mixing brand A ($8 a pound) with brand B ($5 a pound). If the blend is worth $6 a pound, how many pounds of brand A are needed to make 50 pounds of the blend?

## ✦ 27 ✦

Each of the following three words can have another three-letter word added to its beginning to form new words. Can you find at least one three-letter word to make this happen?

**Ear**

**Less**

**Anger**

## ✦ 28 ✦

Find the hidden phrase or title.

## ✦ 29 ✦

If you wrote down all the numbers from 1 to 100, how many times would you write the number 3?

## ✦ 30 ✦

What is $\frac{3}{4}$ of $\frac{1}{2}$ of $4^2$ minus $\frac{1}{2}$ of that result?

## ✦ 31 ✦

Below are six discs stacked on a peg. The object is to reassemble the discs, one by one, in the same order on another peg, using the smallest number of moves. No larger disc can be placed on a smaller disc. How many moves will it take?

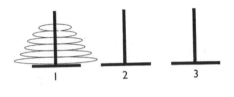

## ✦ 32 ✦

From the word "service," see if you can create 15 new words.

## ✦ 33 ✦

Below is a list of numbers with accompanying codes. Can you decipher the code and determine the number on the last line?

| Number | Code Number |
|--------|-------------|
| 589 | 521 |
| 724 | 386 |
| 1346 | 9764 |
| ? | 485 |

## ✦  34  ✦

Which is greater, a single discount of 12 percent or two successive discounts of 6 percent—or are they the same?

## ✦  35  ✦

Find the hidden phrase or title.

## ✦  36  ✦

Here's a fun and challenging puzzle for those who remember their algebra. Evaluate the following:

$$\frac{x+y}{x^2+y^2} \; \times \; \frac{x}{x-y} \; \div \; \frac{(x+y)^2}{x^4-y^4} \; - \; x$$

## ✦  37  ✦

Below is a sentence based on moving the letters of the alphabet in a consistent manner. See if you can crack the code and come up with the right answer.

### BRX  DUH  D  JHQLXV.

## ✦  38  ✦

The geometric figure below can be divided with one straight line into two parts that will fit together to make a perfect square. Draw that line by connecting two of the numbers.

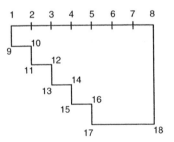

## ✦  39  ✦

The number six is considered a "perfect" number because its factors add up exactly to the number itself (3 + 2 + 1 = 6). What is the next perfect number?

Find the hidden phrase or title.

## ✦ 41 ✦

Some pibs are dals.
All dals are zons.
Some zons are rews.
Some rews are dals.
Therefore, some pibs are definitely rews.

Is the above conclusion true or false?

## ✦ 42 ✦

Which is larger: one-third times one-third of a dozen dozen, or one-third dozen halved and cubed?

## ✦ 43 ✦

The *Genesee Flyer* leaves the station at 60 miles per hour. After three hours, the *Seneca Streamer* leaves the same station at 75 miles per hour, moving in the same direction on an adjacent track. Both trains depart the station at milepost 0. At what milepost will the *Streamer* draw even with the *Flyer*?

## ✦ 44 ✦

A cyclist can ride four different routes from East Klopper to Wickly. There are eight different routes from Wickly to Ganzoon. From Ganzoon to Poscatool, there are three different routes. How many different combinations of routes from East Klopper to Poscatool can the cyclist take? (Do not consider going directly from East Klopper to Poscatool: all routes pass through Wickly, Ganzoon, and Poscatool.)

## ✦ 45 ✦

Kelsey has flipped a penny 17 times in a row, and every time it has landed on heads. What are the chances that the next throw will land on heads?

## ✦ 46 ✦

The ratio of $^3/_7$ to $^4/_9$ is which of the following:

**a.** $\dfrac{8}{9}$

**b.** $\dfrac{35}{36}$

**c.** $\dfrac{3}{4}$

**d.** $\dfrac{27}{28}$

**e.** 1 to 1

## ✦ 47 ✦

Find the hidden phrase or title.

### ✦ 48 ✦

Can you place a symbol between the two numbers below to create a number greater than 4, but less than 5?

**4 5**

### ✦ 49 ✦

Below is a teeter-totter with a 5-pound weight placed 10 feet from the fulcrum and a 6-pound weight placed 5 feet from the fulcrum. On the right side of the fulcrum is a 16-pound weight that needs to be placed in order to balance the weights on the left side. How many feet from the fulcrum should the 16-pound weight be placed?

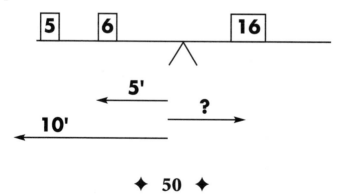

### ✦ 50 ✦

A box of chocolates can be divided equally among 3, 6, or 11 people. What is the smallest number of chocolates the box can contain?

## ✦ 51 ✦

The following puzzle is one of analytical reasoning. See if you can determine the relationships between the figures and the words to find solutions to the two unknowns.

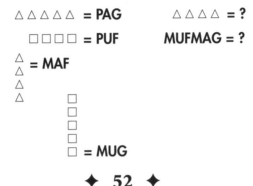

## ✦ 52 ✦

Find the hidden phrase or title.

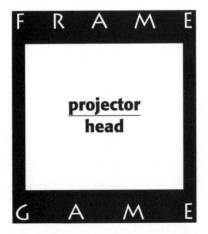

## ✦ 53 ✦

Given the initial letters of the missing words, complete this sentence.

### It is 212 D F at which W B.

## ✦ 54 ✦

Find the missing letter in the following series:

### 2  T  4  F  8  E  16  S  32  T  64  ?

## ✦ 55 ✦

See if you can match each word in the left-column with its meaning in the right-hand column:

|   |   |
|---|---|
| 1. Unctuous | a. Study of the universe |
| 2. Riparian | b. Relating to the bank of a lake or river |
| 3. Porcine | c. An interlacing network, as of blood vessels |
| 4. Plexus | d. An upright post |
| 5. Platitude | e. Fertilize |
| 6. Cosmology | f. Briskness |
| 7. Concatenation | g. Relating to swine |
| 8. Alacrity | h. A series connected by links |
| 9. Fecundate | i. A trite remark |
| 10. Newel | j. Oily |

## ✦ 56 ✦

Which figure does not belong with the other four figures?

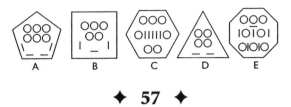

## ✦ 57 ✦

I recently returned from a trip. Today is Friday. I returned four days before the day after the day before tomorrow. On what day did I return?

## ✦ 58 ✦

Find the hidden phrase or title.

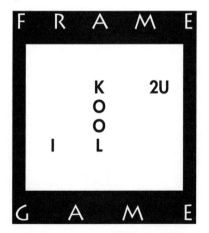

## ✦ 59 ✦

A microscopic slide has 7,500 bacteria dying at a rate of 150 per hour. Another slide has 4,500 bacteria increasing at a rate of 50 per hour. In how many hours will the bacterial count on both slides be the same?

## ✦ 60 ✦

A man told his friend, "Four years from now I'll be twice as old as I was fourteen years ago." How old is the man?

## ✦ 61 ✦

Which figure does not belong with the others, and why?

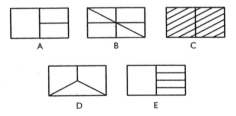

## ✦ 62 ✦

The probability of drawing the Ace of Spades from a deck of 52 playing cards is 1 in 52. What is the probability of drawing the Ace, King, and Queen of Spades on three consecutive draws?

## ✦ 63 ✦

Find the hidden phrase or title.

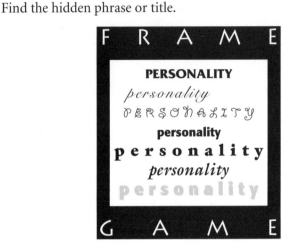

## ✦ 64 ✦

Sometimes things that are mathematically or scientifically true seem impossible. You may think this is one of them. Can you guess what a cubic yard of water weights?

**17 pounds**

**170 pounds**

**1,700 pounds**

**500 pounds**

**98.8 pounds**

## ✦ 65 ✦

If a team wins 60 percent of its games in the first third of a season, what percentage of the remaining games must it win to finish the season having won 80 percent of the games?

## ✦ 66 ✦

Given the initial letters of the missing words, complete the following sentence.

### There are 50 S in the U S F.

## ✦ 67 ✦

If ½ of 24 were 8, what would ⅓ of 18 be?

## ✦ 68 ✦

In this "trickle down" puzzle, you must change one letter of each succeeding word, starting at the top, to arrive at the word at the bottom. There may be more than one way to solve this—use your creativity!

**P A R T**

───────

───────

**W I N E**

## ✦ 69 ✦

Find the hidden phrase or title.

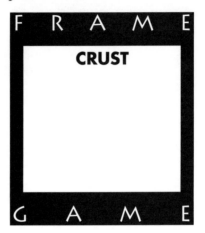

## ✦ 70 ✦

Solve this puzzle without using a pencil or calculator:

$$1 \times 1 = 1$$
$$11 \times 11 = 121$$
$$111 \times 111 = 12{,}321$$
$$1{,}111 \times 1{,}111 = \ ?$$

### ✦ 71 ✦

Find the hidden phrase or title.

### ✦ 72 ✦

There are six murks in a bop, eight bops in a farg, and three fargs in a yump. What is the number of murks in a yump divided by the number of bops in a yump?

### ✦ 73 ✦

If the volume of a cube is 729 cubic feet, how many cubic yards is it?

## ✦ 74 ✦

What is the missing number in the triangle on the right?

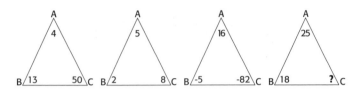

## ✦ 75 ✦

If three pears and four oranges cost $.39 and four pears and three oranges cost $.38, how much does one pear cost?

## ✦ 76 ✦

What is the missing number in this grid?

| 15 | 81 | 168 |
|----|----|-----|
| 23 | 111 | ? |
| 5 | 27 | 56 |

## ✦ 77 ✦

If I quadrupled one-fifth of a fraction and multiplied it by that fraction, I would get one-fifth. What is the original fraction?

*Hint:* There are two answers.

### ✦ 78 ✦

A six-piece band has agreed that the entire band will be paid $1,225 per gig. But the leader of the band is paid twice as much as each of the other five musicians. How much does the leader earn each gig?

### ✦ 79 ✦

Find the hidden phrase or title.

### ✦ 80 ✦

What's the missing number next to the letter "E"?

**P7    H4    O6    N6    E?**

## ✦ 81 ✦

Find the hidden phrase or title.

## ✦ 82 ✦

In a foreign language, *fol birta klar* means "shine red apples." *Pirt klar farn* means "big red bicycles," and *obirts fol pirt* means "shine bicycles often." How would you say "big apples" in this language?

## ✦ 83 ✦

Find three consecutive numbers such that the sum of the first number and the third number is 124.

### ✦ 84 ✦

If $16_a = 20$ and $36_a = 32$, what does $26_a$ equal?

### ✦ 85 ✦

Find the hidden phrase or title.

### ✦ 86 ✦

What nine-letter word is written in the square below? You may start at any letter and go in any direction, but don't go back over any letter.

$$\begin{array}{ccc} T & E & M \\ R & C & O \\ I & G & E \end{array}$$

### ✦ 87 ✦

Can you position four squares of equal size in such a way that you end up with five squares of equal size?

### ✦ 88 ✦

At a reception, one-fourth of the guests departed at a certain time. Later, two-fifths of the remaining guests departed. Even later, three-fourths of those guests departed. If nine people were left, how many were originally at the party?

### ✦ 89 ✦

Find the hidden phrase or title.

## ✦ 90 ✦

In spelling out numbers, you don't often find the letter "a." Quickly now, what is the first number, counting upward from zero, in which this letter appears?

## ✦ 91 ✦

Find the hidden phrase or title.

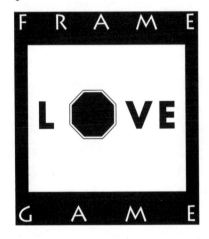

## 92 ✦

With five fair tosses of a penny, what is the probability of its landing on heads five times in a row?

*Hint:* Remember, the tosses constitute a sequence of events.

## ✦ 93 ✦

What physical characteristics do the following capital letters share in common?

**A H I M O T U V W X Y**

## ✦ 94 ✦

What comes next in the following series?

**240  120  40  10  2 ?**

## ✦ 95 ✦

A triangle has sides of *X*, *Y*, and *Z*. Which of the following statements is true?

**1. X–Y is always equal to 2.**
**2. Y–X is always less than Z.**
**3. Z–X is always greater than Y.**
**4. X + Y is always greater than Z + Y.**
**5. No correct answer is given.**

## ✦ 96 ✦

Given four points in space and connecting three points at a time to determine a plane (extending to infinity), what is the maximum number of lines that will result from all intersections?

### ✦ 97 ✦

Find the hidden phrase or title.

### ✦ 98 ✦

What is the missing number in the circle below?

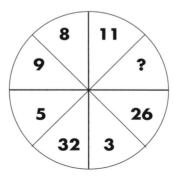

## ✦ 99 ✦

In this "trickle-down" puzzle, start at the top and change one letter to each succeeding word to arrive at the word at the bottom.

**F A S T**

_____

_____

_____

**M I N D**

## ✦ 100 ✦

A cube measuring four inches on each side is painted blue all over and is then sliced into one-inch cubes. How many of the smaller cubes are blue on three sides?

## ✦ 101 ✦

When purchased together, a pair of binoculars and the case cost $100. If the binoculars cost $90 more than the case, how much does the case cost? Give yourself about 15 seconds to solve this.

## ✦ 102 ✦

A clock strikes six in five seconds. How long will it take to strike eleven?

## ✦ 103 ✦

Find the hidden phrase or title.

## ✦ 104 ✦

Sammy Johnson has two sisters, but the Johnson girls have no brother. How can this be?

## ✦ 105 ✦

Decipher this cryptogram:

### T'M QPFASQ RS TD LATOPMSOLATP.
### —G. N. KTSOMY

## ✦ 106 ✦

Given the initial letters of the missing words, complete this sentence.

### There are 9 I in a B G.

## ✦ 107 ✦

What three-letter word can be placed in front of each of the following words to make four new words?

### MAN

### HOUSE

### CAP

### AM

## ✦ 108 ✦

How many squares of any size are in the figure below? Be careful; there may be more than you think!

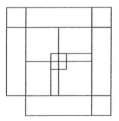

## ✦ 109 ✦

Find the hidden phrase or title.

## ✦ 110 ✦

Imagine we were to adopt a new number system based on 13 instead of 10. Show a way in which the first 13 numbers might be written.

## ✦ 111 ✦

Electric current is measured in amps, resistance is measured in ohms, and power is measured in watts. What is frequency measured in?

### ✦ 112 ✦

Find the hidden phrase or title.

### ✦ 113 ✦

Unscramble the following word:

**LAMPANETRYARI**

### ✦ 114 ✦

What is the missing letter in the last circle?

## ✦ 115 ✦

How would you write 944 in Roman numerals?

## ✦ 116 ✦

If 2,048 people entered a statewide singles tennis tournament, how many total matches would be played, including the championship match?

## ✦ 117 ✦

Decipher this cryptogram phrase:

**SEO LXABXGS JW EMLLGQOBB.**

## ✦ 118 ✦

If you have a two-in-five chance of winning something, what are your odds?

## ✦ 119 ✦

What four-letter word can be placed in front of each of the following words to form new words?

**LINE**

**PHONE**

**WATERS**

## ✦ 120 ✦

Find the hidden phrase or title.

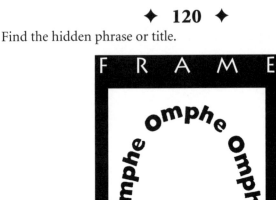

## ✦ 121 ✦

The numbers in each box below have a relationship in common. Can you identify that relationship and find the missing number?

| 2, 11 | 4, 67 | 5, 128 | 3, ? |
|-------|-------|--------|------|

## ✦ 122 ✦

Complete the following analogy:

**B-sharp is to C as Bach is to ?**

### ✦ 123 ✦

How many triangles can you find in this diagram?

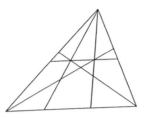

### ✦ 124 ✦

Find the hidden phrase or title.

# ✦ 125 ✦

See if you can match the legal terms in the left column with the definitions in the right column:

1. Arbitration
    a. A rule in which the court takes notice of facts that are known with certainty to be true

2. Exculpatory
    b. Submission of controversies to a third party, whose decisions are usually binding

3. Judicial notice
    c. A doctrine providing a party an equitable defense where neglected rights are sought to be enforced against the party

4. Laches
    d. A method of settling disputes with a neutral party in which the neutral party is a link between the disputing parties

5. Probative
    e. A type of evidence that tends to clear or excuse a defendant from fault

6. Tort
    f. Tending to prove a proposition or to persuade one of the truth of an allegation

7. Mediation
    g. A private or civil wrong

# ✦ 126 ✦

How many different words can you make from the word "numbers"?

## ✦ 127 ✦

The series below, containing the numbers 1 through 10, can be completed by placing the missing numbers, 2 and 3, at the end. Which comes first, the 2 or the 3? Why?

**8   5   4   9   1   7   6   10   ?   ?**

## ✦ 128 ✦

Find the hidden phrase or title.

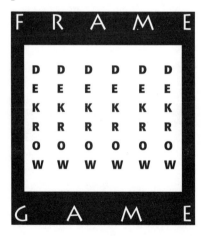

## ✦ 129 ✦

Given the initial letters of the missing words, complete this sentence.

**There are 6 P on the S of D.**

## ✦ 130 ✦

Which figure below does not belong with the rest, and why?

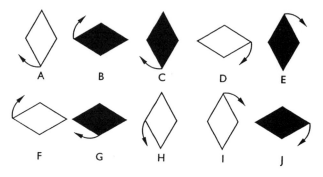

## ✦ 131 ✦

Find the hidden phrase or title.

### ✦ 132 ✦

What is the value of Z in the diagram below?

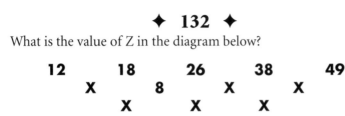

### ✦ 133 ✦

Here's a four-letter "trickle-down" puzzle. See if you can come up with the three missing words, each with only one letter changed from the previous word, to arrive at the word KEEP. (There may be more than one set of correct answers.)

**F E A R**
———
———
———
**K E E P**

### ✦ 134 ✦

Try your luck at this series. To arrive at each succeeding number, squaring of numbers is required.

**0  6  6  20  20  42  42  ?**

### ✦ 135 ✦

Find the hidden phrase or title.

### ✦ 136 ✦

Two of the five phrases listed below are equivalent. Which are they?

        **a. 14 square yards**

        **b. 14 yards square**

        **c. 127 square feet**

        **d. 196 square yards**

        **e. 206 yards squared**

### ✦ 137 ✦

Given the initial letters of the missing words, complete this sentence.

**There are 360 D in a S.**

### ✦ 138 ✦

Find the hidden phrase or title.

### ✦ 139 ✦

Unscramble the following word:

**T E S I A L L E C**

## ✦ 140 ✦

Find the hidden phrase or title.

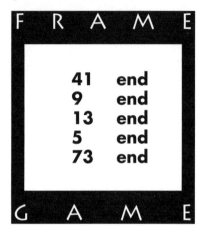

## ✦ 141 ✦

A palindrome is a word or phrase spelled the same both forward and backward, such as noon, dad, deed, and sees. Can you think of three or more palindromic words of at least five letters?

## ✦ 142 ✦

In a golf tournament, you're part of the final group on the last day. The first prize is $250,000. One member of the foursome (but not you!) sinks a 50-foot putt on the 72nd hole to win the tournament. You are ecstatic! In fact, that person is the one you hoped would win all along. You didn't have a bet on the outcome, so why are you happy that this golfer won?

### ✦ 143 ✦

Change one letter of each succeeding word, starting at the top, to
arrive at the word at the bottom.

**M E A L**

—————

—————

—————

—————

**B O O K**

### ✦ 144 ✦

Find the hidden phrase or title.

FRAME

cheek

cheek

GAME

## ✦ 145 ✦

If it were three hours later than it is now, it would be twice as long until midnight as it would be if it were four hours later. What time is it now?

## ✦ 146 ✦

Given the initial letters of the missing words, complete this sentence:

### There are 9 P on a B T.

## ✦ 147 ✦

Shown below are nine one-inch-long matches. Arrange the matches to create three squares that are the same size.

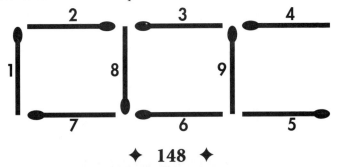

## ✦ 148 ✦

What is the missing number in this series?

*Hint*: Think of a new approach, rather than going from left to right.

### 13  4  22  37  44  10  42  ?  15  30  48  39

## ✦ 149 ✦

The meanings of the following five words can change with the addition of a certain common prefix. Can you find that prefix?

**stance — station — title — tract — scribe**

## ✦ 150 ✦

Nancy is Goldie's father's son's wife's daughter. What relation is Goldie to Nancy?

## ✦ 151 ✦

Find the hidden phrase or title.

## ✦ 152 ✦

The following is an unusual number series. Don't try to solve it in a normal manner. Take a different route—it might be just a fraction of what you think.

*Hint:* In any event, don't take longer than a fortnight to solve this.

### 0 7 1 4 2 8 ?

## ✦ 153 ✦

If one-half of 48 were 32, what would one-third of 18 be?

## ✦ 154 ✦

Find the hidden phrase or title.

## ✦ 155 ✦

Following is the beginning and ending of a word chain. By removing one letter at a time, see if you can come up with a new word on each line. No plurals, please!

**S T R A I N**

– – – – –

– – – –

– – –

– –

–

## ✦ 156 ✦

If you were to lay three identical rectangles on top of each other, what would be the maximum number of resulting intersections? An intersection must be the crossing of two and only two lines; do not include corners. For this puzzle, size the rectangles in a 1:2 proportion. Here's what a start might look like (but it doesn't give us the maximum!):

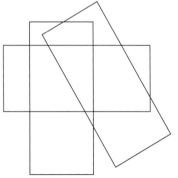

### ✦ 157 ✦

What are the chances of getting at least two heads when flipping a penny three times?

### ✦ 158 ✦

What two numbers will give you an answer of 10 when one is subtracted from the other and an answer of 2,000 when they are multiplied together?

### ✦ 159 ✦

Find the hidden phrase or title.

## ✦ 160 ✦

Quickly now, how long is 1,000,000 seconds? Your answer should be in days.

## ✦ 161 ✦

How many digits must be changed in the following addition problem to make the sum 173?

$$
\begin{array}{r}
68 \\
99 \\
+ \ 81 \\
\hline
\end{array}
$$

## ✦ 162 ✦

Which of the given choices is the next term in this sequence?

**PRS, PRT, PRU, PST, PSU, _____**

**PSV**
**PSR**
**PUT**
**PTU**
**PUS**

## ✦ 163 ✦

Unscramble the following letters to come up with a word that means "puzzle":

**E N I T R A E S R A B**

## ✦ 164 ✦

The numbers in the left-hand column were given the security code numbers in the right-hand column. Can you crack the code to fill in the missing number?

| | |
|---|---|
| 537 | 1463 |
| 892 | 1108 |
| 1615 | 385 |
| 722 | ? |

## ✦ 165 ✦

What is ½ of ¼ of ²⁄₉ of ³⁄₇ of 84?

## ✦ 166 ✦

In the series 2, 4, 8, 16, 32, 64…, can you come up with a formula using the letter n to find the sum of the series?

## ✦ 167 ✦

Imagine a cube 3 inches by 3 inches through space. Now imagine that this cube is divided into 27 one-inch cubes. The maximum number of cubes visible to an observer at any one moment is 19. With a 4 × 4 cube further subdivided into 64 cubes, the maximum number of cubes that can be seen by an observer at any one moment is 37. How many cubes can be observed in a 5 × 5 cube (125 smaller cubes total) and a 6 × 6 cube (216 smaller cubes total)?

## ✦ 168 ✦

Below is a spatial/visual analogy.

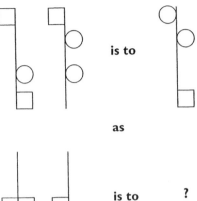

is to

as

is to          ?

## ✦ 169 ✦

What comes next in the following sequence?

### 1/7  4/9  2/8  5/10  3/9  6/11  ?/?

## ✦ 170 ✦

Given the initial letters of the missing words, complete this sentence.

### There are 2 P in a Q.

## ✦ 171 ✦

Find the hidden phrase or title.

## ✦ 172 ✦

What conclusion, if any, can you draw from the following?

**No humans are not mammals.**
**No mammals live on Mamal.**
**Adam Mammale, a former pilot who once lived**
**in Detroit, can live only on Mamal.**

## ✦ 173 ✦

Fill in the letters to complete the following word, which means "fulfilled, achieved."

**C O __ __ __ E __ E __**

## ✦ 174 ✦

Find the hidden phrase or title.

## ✦ 175 ✦

Change one letter at a time, forming a new word each time, to get from the first word to the last.

**PARTY**
———
———
———
———
**DUNES**

Find the hidden phrase or title.

When you decode the message spelled out in the following three triangles, it becomes a riddle. What number answers that riddle?

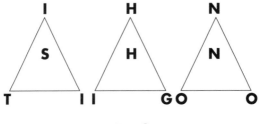

### ✦ 178 ✦

Here is a number series puzzle that looks complicated but that actually has a very easy solution.

*Hint:* Only a certain percentage will solve this.

**100 – 100 – 90 – 72 – 50.4 – 30.24 – _____**

### ✦ 179 ✦

Find the hidden phrase or title.

### ✦ 180 ✦

Decipher the following cryptogram:

**PNOFNOF NO SBT CUNO**

### ✦ 181 ✦

Here is an example of three vulgar fractions with the same value that use all the digits from 1 to 9 once and only once:

$$\frac{2}{4} = \frac{3}{6} = \frac{79}{158}$$

Can you find three other such fractions of equal value that use these nine digits only once?

### ✦ 182 ✦

Find the hidden phrase or title.

## ✦  183  ✦

Here's a different twist on a cube puzzle. The diagram shows six connected squares that need to be folded into a cube. Next to the squares are four views of the same cube. Can you fill in the six squares with the appropriate figures?

## ✦  184  ✦

Find the hidden phrase or title.

## ✦ 185 ✦

Chordorfs are less numerous than chlordorfs. Chlorodorfs are more numerous than chlordorfs. Chloroodorfs are less numerous than chlordorfs. If you were to list the most numerous of the preceding four items, from the top down, where would chloroodorfs fit?

## ✦ 186 ✦

What is the next number in the following series?

**1, 2, 6, 30, 60, 180, 900,**
**1,800, 5,400, ——**

## ✦ 187 ✦

Joseph is my uncle's sister's grandaughter's son. What is the closest possible relationship I can have to Joseph?

## ✦ 188 ✦

How may words can you find in the word "confession"?
(No fair using plurals.)

## ✦ 189 ✦

If 30 baseballs are needed for 9 pitchers over 2 days of practice, what is the number of baseballs needed for 11 pitchers over 3 days of practice?

### ✦ 190 ✦

Find the hidden phrase or title.

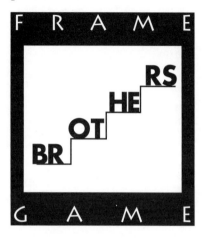

### ✦ 191 ✦

One of the following does not belong with the others. Which one, and why?

*Hint:* Don't be concerned about whether an item grows above or below the ground.

**CUCUMBERS — ZUCCHINI — PUMPKINS**

**–EGGPLANTS–CARROTS**

## ✦ 192 ✦

One of the four cubes pictured below the six connected squares is impossible to make from the six squares. The other three are correct views when the six squares are folded properly into a cube. Which is the odd one out?

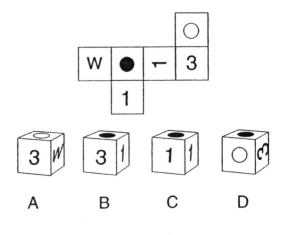

## ✦ 193 ✦

Joe takes three-fifths of a bag of candy. Bob has three-fourths of Pete's share of the remaining candy. What fraction of the total number of pieces of candy does Pete have?

## ✦ 194 ✦

What is the value of F in the following system of equations?

$$
\begin{aligned}
A + B &= Z &\quad (1) \\
Z + P &= T &\quad (2) \\
T + A &= F &\quad (3) \\
B + P + F &= 30 &\quad (4) \\
A &= 8 &\quad (5)
\end{aligned}
$$

## ✦ 195 ✦

Determine the relationships between the pictures and the letters to find the solutions:

○○○ = DAGY   ○ (over) ○ = CABY   1) = ?

◇ ◇ = DEBY   ◇ (over) ◇ = CEGI   2) DEBICAGY = ?

○○ (overlapping) = DABI

## ✦ 196 ✦

Can you quickly write down the numbers 1 through 5 so that no two consecutive numbers are next to one another? The first number is not 1, and the second, third, and fourth numbers must increase in value.

## ✦ 197 ✦

Arrange the four squares below to create five squares of the same size. You cannot interlock or overlap the squares.

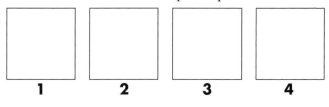

**1**    **2**    **3**    **4**

## ✦ 198 ✦

The following words can all be transformed into new words by prefixing the same three letters, in the same order, at the beginning of the words. What are the three letters?

| | |
|---|---|
| _ _ _ | **PENT** |
| _ _ _ | **RATE** |
| _ _ _ | **VICE** |
| _ _ _ | **VILE** |

## ✦ 199 ✦

What comes next in this number sequence?

*Hint:* Get primed for this puzzle.

**5    8    26    48    122    ?**

## ✦ 200 ✦

Find the hidden phrase or title.

## ✦ 201 ✦

The words *assign* and *stalactite* form a relationship that produces the word *ignite* in parentheses. Can you find a similar relationship between the words *double* and *stationary* that will form a new word in the blank?

| assign | (ignite) | stalactite |
|--------|----------|------------|
| double | (_____) | stationary |

## ✦ 202 ✦

What is 1,449 in Roman numerals?

## ✦ 203 ✦

Here's a balance puzzle. Where does the 25-lb. weight on this teeter-totter go (how many feet from the fulcrum)?

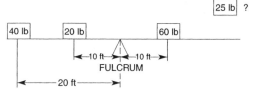

## ✦ 204 ✦

Find the hidden phrase or title.

## ✦ 205 ✦

What is ⅓ divided by ⅕ divided by ⅔ times ⅗?

## ✦ 206 ✦

A group of students at a major university was polled to see which courses they were taking. Sixty-four percent were taking English, 22% were taking a foreign language, and 7% were taking both. What percentage of the students polled were taking neither subject?

## ✦ 207 ✦

You need to match three items, A, B, and C, with three numbers, 1, 2, and 3. But you are given some peculiar information by which to determine how to match them up. From the following rules, can you find a solution?

**(a)  If A is not 1, then C is not 3.**

**(b)  If B is either 2 or 1, then A is 3.**

**(c)  If C is not 2, then A cannot be 3.**

**(d)  If C is not 1, then A is not 3.**

**(e)  If C is 3, then B is not 1 or 2.**

**(f)  If B is 3, then A is not 2.**

## ✦ 208 ✦

Given the initial letters of the missing words, complete this sentence:

**There are 6 O in an I.**

# ✦ 209 ✦

Here is a five-letter "trickle-down" puzzle. Change one letter at a time to reach the final word.

**T I M E R**

———————

———————

———————

**D U N K S**

# ✦ 210 ✦

Find the hidden phrase or title.

## ✦ 211 ✦

Quickly now, solve this puzzle! You are taking a long drink of water. Which happens first?

**The glass is ⁵⁄₁₆ empty.**
**The glass is ⅝ full.**

## ✦ 212 ✦

Quickly now, finish this mathematical analogy:

**⅕ is to 5 as 5 is to ___?___ .**

## ✦ 213 ✦

Find the hidden phrase or title.

## ✦ 214 ✦

There is a certain logic in the following diagram in the placement of the letters around the triangles. What is the missing letter in the last triangle?

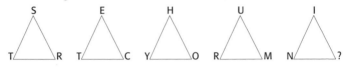

## ✦ 215 ✦

Find the hidden phrase or title.

## ✦ 216 ✦

Judy and Mary are Susan's sister's mother-in-law's son's daughters. What relation is Susan to Judy and Mary?

## ✦ 217 ✦

Bill and Tom played several golf matches against each other in a week. They played for a pizza at each match, but no pizzas were purchased until the end of the week. If at any time during the week Tom and Bill had the same number of wins, those pizzas were canceled. Bill won four matches (but no pizzas), and Tom won three pizzas. How many rounds of golf were played?

## ✦ 218 ✦

Find the hidden phrase or title.

## ✦ 219 ✦

Quickly now, $\frac{1}{7}$ is what percentage of $\frac{3}{11}$?

### ✦ 220 ✦

One way to make eight 8's equal 100 would be as follows:

$$\frac{8888 - 88}{88} = 100$$

Can you devise at least one other way?

### ✦ 221 ✦

How long will it take for you to find three common, everyday words that contain three straight A's? By straight, I mean that they can be separated by consonants, but not by another vowel.

### ✦ 222 ✦

Find the hidden phrase or title.

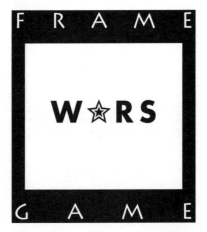

## ✦ 223 ✦

A professional bass fisherman caught 30 bass during a five-day tournament. Each day, he caught three more fish than the day before. How many fish did he catch the first day?

## ✦ 224 ✦

What is the missing number in this grid?

| 12 | 27 | 111 |
|----|----|-----|
| 19 | 39 | ?   |
| 4  | 9  | 37  |

## ✦ 225 ✦

Given the initial letters of the missing words, complete this phrase:

### 86,400 S in a D

*Hint:* You have up to 24 hours to solve this.

## ✦ 226 ✦

Fifteen seconds for this one: Unscramble the following letters to come up with a word game everyone knows.

### B L A B S C E R

How many squares are in the figure below?

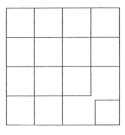

**◆ 228 ◆**

How many numbers are in the following sequence if all terms are included?

**0 3 6 9 12 15 18 ... 960**

**◆ 229 ◆**

Here's an alphametic puzzle that isn't too difficult. See if you can replace the letters with the proper numbers to make this puzzle work.

$$
\begin{array}{r}
\text{H E} \\
\times \text{M E} \\
\hline
\text{B E} \\
\text{Y E} \phantom{0} \\
\hline
\text{E W E}
\end{array}
$$

### ✦ 230 ✦

Find the hidden phrase or title.

### ✦ 231 ✦

There are two boxers. The smaller boxer is an amateur and also the son of the bigger boxer, who is a professional. But the pro boxer is not the amateur's father. Who is the pro?

### ✦ 232 ✦

In a game of craps, you are considering betting that the next roll of the dice is going to produce a 2, a 3, or a 12 (not necessarily a come-out roll). A friend who is quick with probabilities advises you against making this bet. Why?

## ✦ 233 ✦

Shown below are four ways to divide a four-by-four grid in half. Find the other two ways. No diagonals or rotations allowed (for example, #1 turned 90 degrees doesn't count).

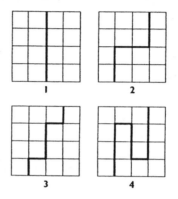

## ✦ 234 ✦

Seven of the following eight words are related. Which is the odd one out and why?

CALCIUM              IODINE

IRON                 MAGNESIUM

PHOSPHOROUS          SELENIUM

TOCOPHEROL           ZINC

### ✦ 235 ✦

If two-fifths of a fraction is doubled and then multiplied by the original fraction, the result is $\frac{1}{15}$. What is the original fraction (positive numbers only)?

### ✦ 236 ✦

Find the hidden phrase or title.

### ✦ 237 ✦

A little knowledge of algebra may help here. You've been given $100 and told to buy 100 candles for a party. The first type of candle costs $0.50, the second $5.50, and the third $9.50. You must purchase exactly 100 candles and spend exactly $100. How many candles of each type will you purchase? There is just one solution.

## ✦ 238 ✦

A palindromic number is one that reads the same forward and backward, such as 8,315,138. There are only three palindromic squares under 1,000. Two of those are $11^2 = 121$ and $22^2 = 484$.

## What is the third palindromic square under 1,000?

## What is the first palindromic square over 1,000?

## ✦ 239 ✦

How many triangles are in the figure below?

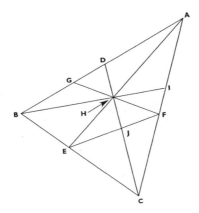

## ✦ 240 ✦

Find the hidden phrase or title.

## ✦ 241 ✦

What is the next letter in the following sequence?

**D – N – O – S – A – J – ?** __

*Hint:* Can time run backward?

## ✦ 242 ✦

From among the integers 1 through 9, can you find six different integers—call them A, B, C, D, E, and F—such that A × B × C = D × E × F?

*Hint:* Don't use 5 or 7.

## ✦ 243 ✦

The letters in several words in the English language lend themselves to being recombined into new words. For example, the word *item* can be transformed into *mite*, and *emit*. The letters of the word *vile* can be rearranged to *live*, *evil*, and *veil*. Try to find a four-letter word that can be changed into four new words (five total, counting your original).

## ✦ 244 ✦

A visitor to a zoo asked the zookeeper how many birds and how many beasts were in a certain section of the zoo. The zookeeper replied: "There are 45 heads and 150 feet, and with that information you should be able to tell me how many of each there are." Can you help the visitor?

## ✦ 245 ✦

Complete the following straightforward math sequence puzzle. It is easier than it appears at first glance.

**240 − 240 − 120 − 40 − 10 − 2 − ?** __

## ✦ 246 ✦

If 28 equals 24 and 68 equals 76, what does 48 equal?

## ✦ 247 ✦

In the figure, line **AB** is parallel to line **CD**, angle Y = 50°, and angle Z = 140°. How big is angle X?

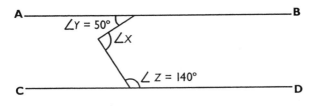

## ✦ 248 ✦

Following is a word written in a code in which each set of two-digit numbers represents a letter. See if you can decipher the word.

**41    51    55    55    32    15    44**

*Hint 1:* Notice that 5 is the highest number used.
*Hint 2:* Think of rows and columns.

## ✦ 249 ✦

Given the initial letters of the missing words, complete the following phrase.

*Hint:* Think of a musical.

### 76 T in the B P

## ✦ 250 ✦

Determine Figure H in the series below.

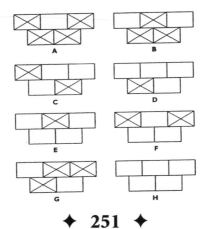

## ✦ 251 ✦

One hundred doctors are attending a medical convention. Each doctor is either a surgeon or a dermatologist. At least one is a dermatologist. Given any two of the doctors, at least one is a surgeon. How many are dermatologists and how many are surgeons?

## ✦ 252 ✦

The five words listed here share a common trait. By playing with the letters of each word, see if you can determine the trait.

*Hint:* The same trait is shared with the words apt, tea, and tar.

**rifle — evil — deal — rats — tale**

## ✦ 253 ✦

Which of the following is larger?

    A. $\frac{1}{3}$ times its cube times a dozen cubed

    B. $\frac{1}{2}$ times its square times a dozen dozen squared divided by
       2 squared times 2 cubed

## ✦ 254 ✦

Here's another alphametic:

After seeing what one round of 18 holes of golf would cost at the new country club, Mary decided that today would be an excellent day to play tennis. How much did the round of golf cost (cart included, of course!)?

$$
\begin{array}{cccc}
S & E & E & S \\
T & E & E & S \\
\underline{F} & \underline{E} & \underline{E} & \underline{S} \\
C & A.S & & H \\
\end{array}
$$

## ✦ 255 ✦

What is the next number in this sequence?

**1 4 9 7 7 9 4 1 9 ?**

## ✦ 256 ✦

If two gallons of paint are needed to cover all sides of one cube, how many gallons are needed to cover all exposed surfaces of the figure below? Include surfaces on which the figure is resting.

*Hint:* There are no hidden cubes.

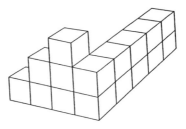

## ✦ 257 ✦

Find the hidden phrase or title.

## ✦ 258 ✦

What are the values of R and S?

$$Q + M = C$$
$$C + K = R$$
$$R + Q = S$$
$$M + K + S = 40$$
$$Q = 8$$

## ✦ 259 ✦

Decipher the following cryptogram.

**AGEGLLGO CM BUGAJNL IBD.**

## ✦ 260 ✦

Using the number 4 twice and only twice, can you come up with the number 12? You may use any math symbol or sign you wish. Remember, only the number 4 may be used, and only twice.

## ✦ 261 ✦

Complete this wheel:

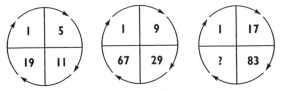

## ✦ 262 ✦

Find the hidden phrase or title.

## ✦ 263 ✦

What is the next figure in the following series?

$$\text{I} \quad \exists \text{E} \quad \delta \quad \text{K} \quad \varphi$$

## ✦ 264 ✦

One-fifth of a pound of chocolate is balanced perfectly by two-fifths of a block of the same chocolate. What is the weight of the whole block of chocolate?

## ✦ 265 ✦

Find the hidden phrase or title.

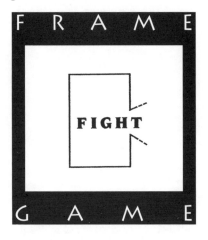

## ✦ 266 ✦

A man played roulette every day and lost money every day. As the story goes, a fortune teller had put a curse on him that he would lose every time he played roulette. For the ten years since, he has been losing consistently every day, yet he is a very wealthy man who has a loving wife and family. In fact, his wife has even accompanied him daily to the roulette table, where he bets either red or black only. How could this family be so wealthy?

## ✦ 267 ✦

You see here a two-dimensional front view and a two-dimensional top view of a three-dimensional object. Can you sketch what the object looks like in three dimensions?

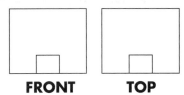

**FRONT**          **TOP**

## ✦ 268 ✦

What comes next in this sequence?

$^1/_1$  $^9/_8$  $^5/_4$  $^4/_3$  $^3/_2$  $^5/_3$  $^{15}/_8$  $^?/$

*Hint:* Think of music.

## ✦ 269 ✦

Unscramble the following:

**T  D  I  L  U  E  A  T**

## ✦ 270 ✦

Six hours ago, it was two hours later than three hours before midnight. What time is it?

### ✦ 271 ✦

Find the hidden phrase or title.

### ✦ 272 ✦

The box pictured here has been folded together from one of the four choices given. Which is the correct choice?

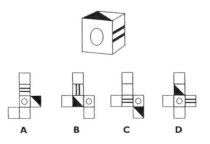

Find the hidden phrase or title.

## ✦ 274 ✦

A jeweler is offering to cut rare gems into fractions to sell to distributors. For $20 a distributor can purchase 1/40 of an ounce, or for $40 she can purchase 1/20 of an ounce. Many of the distributors want another cutting in between these two offerings. An enterprising young dealer opens a store across the street and offers 1/30 of an ounce for $30. Fair enough, right? Where would you buy your gems, or does it even make a difference?

## ✦ 275 ✦

Find the hidden phrase or title.

## ✦ 276 ✦

What three-letter word can be added to the beginning of these words to form four new words?

**RACKS**
**FLY**
**RAGE**
**BELL**

## ✦ 277 ✦

What is the largest sum of money you can have in coins and not be able to make change for a dollar?

## ✦ 278 ✦

Fill in the blank:

**Amelia is the daughter of Amanda.
Amanda is the _____ of Amelia's mother.**

## ✦ 279 ✦

Here is a sequence puzzle consisting of the numbers 0 through 9.
Complete the sequence by filling in the remaining numbers. How
is the pattern formed?

**3    6    9    2    5    8    1    4    ?    ?**

## ✦ 280 ✦

If satellite *y* takes three years to make one revolution and satellite
*x* takes five years to make one revolution, in how many years will
they both be exactly in line as they are now?

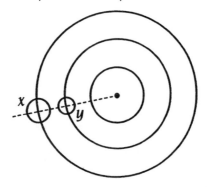

## ✦ 281 ✦

Find the hidden phrase or title.

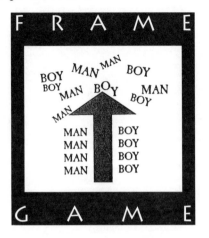

## ✦ 282 ✦

The houses on a street are numbered 1, 2, 3, 4, 5, etc., up one side of the street; then the numbers continue consecutively on the other side of the street and work their way back to be opposite number 1. If house number 12 is opposite house number 29, how many houses are there on both sides of the street?

## ✦ 283 ✦

If Alicia is three times as old as Amy will be when Alex is as old as Alicia is now, who is the second oldest? Can you give their ages now?

## ✦ 284 ✦

Maria covered the first half of a bicycle race at 20 miles per hour. The second half of the race was a return over the same route, and her return speed was 30 miles per hour. What was Maria's average speed for the entire trip? Take your time with this.

## ✦ 285 ✦

One of the five following figures does not belong with the rest. Which one is it, and why?

A          B          C          D          E

## ✦ 286 ✦

A boat is coming downstream at 30 mph. On its return, it travels at 10 mph. The trip downstream is three hours shorter than the trip upstream. How far is it from the beginning of the trip to the turnaround point downstream?

## ✦ 287 ✦

A certain pipe can fill a swimming pool in two hours; another pipe can fill it in five hours; a third pipe can empty the pool in six hours. With all three pipes turned on exactly at the same time, and starting with an empty pool, how long will it take to fill the pool?

## ✦ 288 ✦

What 12-letter word is written in the block below? Start with any letter and move one letter at a time, in any direction, but don't go back over any letter!

```
O   I   R   T
G   N   E   T
O   M   R   Y
```

## ✦ 289 ✦

Fill in the two missing numbers in the following boxes.

*Hint:* Think outside the boxes.

| 1 | 6 | 3 | 6 | 7 |
|---|---|---|---|---|
| 2 | ? | 1 | 9 | 8 |
| 4 | 3 | 5 | 6 | ? |

## ✦ 290 ✦

Can you find 50 different words in the word "arithmetic"?

## ✦ 291 ✦

Given the initial letters of the missing words, complete this sentence.

**There are 5 S to a P.**

### ✦ 292 ✦

Find the hidden phrase or title.

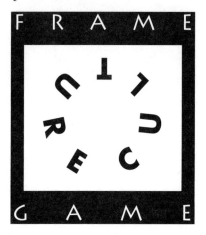

### ✦ 293 ✦

The proportion of southpaws among pitchers is greater than among players in general. Is there a statement that can be made for certain about the proportion of pitchers among left-handers compared to all ballplayers? Is it greater, smaller, or the same, or is there not enough information to tell?

### ✦ 294 ✦

What is the next number in this sequence?

**5   6   8   7   9   3   4   5   10   2   11   ?**

## ✦ 295 ✦

Can you discover what is going on in the following figures? What is the relationship among the circles, squares, and dividing line that determines the respective numbers? What number goes with the sixth figure?

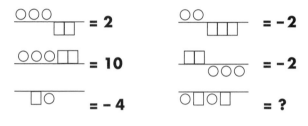

## ✦ 296 ✦

Find the hidden phrase or title.

## ✦ 297 ✦

Draw a square. Now divide the square into four equal, congruent parts with three straight lines. None of the lines may cross each other within the square.

## ✦ 298 ✦

Find the hidden phrase or title.

## ✦ 299 ✦

Quickly now, which of the following symbols denotes mercury in the periodic table of the elements?

**Me    Mr    Hg    Hr    My**

## ✦ 300 ✦

Change the position of one match stick to correct the following equation.

*Hint:* Think Roman.

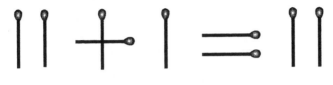

## ✦ 301 ✦

Move from the first word to the last in six moves, changing one letter each time to form a new word.

**TREAT**

—————

—————

—————

—————

—————

**BLOND**

## ✦ 302 ✦

Here is a word that needs to be unscrambled into an ordinary word recognizable to most anyone:

## CRICKARFREE

## ✦ 303 ✦

Find the hidden phrase or title.

## ✦ 304 ✦

At a reception, one-third of the guests departed at a certain time. Later, two-fifths of the remaining guests departed. Even later, two-thirds of those guests departed. If six people were left, how many were originally at the party?

## ✦ 305 ✦

An eagle, an elephant, and a walleye have two. A tiger, a moose, a bear, a turtle, and a snake have one. Humans don't have any. What are we talking about?

### ✦ 306 ✦

The dreaded cube-eaters from the fourth dimension descend upon a stack of 27 identical sugar cubes. Cube-eaters can only eat to the center of a cube. When they reach the center, they always make a 90° turn and proceed to the next cube. They never reenter a cube. If a cube-eater enters at location A, what is the minimum number of cubes it will eat through to reach the cube at location B?

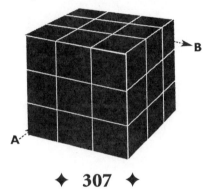

### ✦ 307 ✦

How many individual cubes are in this stack of cubes? Assume that all rows and columns are complete unless you actually see them end.

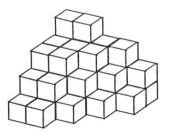

Find the hidden phrase or title.

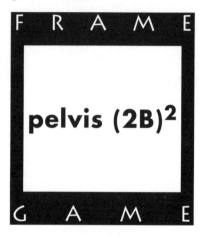

✦ 309 ✦

You have the four kings and four queens from a deck of cards. Place the queens on top of the kings facedown in one stack. Pick up the stack, and starting with the top card (queen), place it faceup on a table. Take the second card and place it facedown on the bottom of the cards in your hand; place the third card faceup on the table, the fourth card on the bottom, and so on, until all cards are faceup. What is the order of the cards that are faceup?

## ✦ 310 ✦

Five types of flowers grow in five gardens on five different streets. Given the following information, determine which flowers grow where.

1. The Smiths do not grow violets.
2. The Morgans grow peonies; they do not live on 2nd Street.
3. The Parks live on 3rd Street.
4. Begonias bloom on 4th Street.
5. Roses do not grow on 5th Street.
6. The Johnsons do not live on 1st Street.
7. The Rosens do not grow daffodils.
8. The Johnsons grow roses.
9. Daffodils grow on 1st Street.

## ✦ 311 ✦

What is the missing number in this sequence?

**(7, 8) (19, 27) (37, 64) (61, 125)**

**(91, 216) (?, 343)**

## ✦ 312 ✦

Given the initial letters of the missing words, complete this sentence.

**There are 14 D in a F.**

Find the hidden phrase or title.

## ✦ 314 ✦

See if you can unscramble the following words to make a sensible sentence out of them.

**Last they say who best laughs or, he laughs so.**

## ✦ 315 ✦

Unscramble these letters to make a word:

**RALLEAPL**

## ✦ 316 ✦

Here's another "trickle-down" puzzle. Change one letter on each line to reach the final word. There may be more than one way to do this puzzle.

**PEST**

———

———

———

**BATS**

## ✦ 317 ✦

Find the hidden phrase or title.

### ✦ 318 ✦

Below are three intersecting circles that have a maximum of seven bounded areas that are not further subdivided. What is the maximum number of bounded areas that result when six circles are intersected?

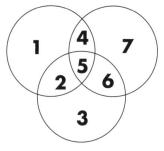

### ✦ 319 ✦

Here is a form of syllogism. Assume that the first three statements are true and then determine whether the fourth statement, the conclusion, is valid or false. That's all there is to it!

**Some *zers* are *tifs*.**
**All *tifs* are *xorts*.**
**Some *xorts* are *wols*.**
**Therefore, some *zers* are definitely *wols*.**

### ✦ 320 ✦

If 14 equals 12 and 34 equals 38, what does 24 equal?

## ✦ 321 ✦

There is an old puzzle that asks you to come up with the longest word you can create using only the letter keys from the top row of a typewriter. Those letters are: Q, W, E, R, T, Y, U, I, O, and P. The solution to that puzzle is the 10-letter word TYPEWRITER.

Here's a new twist. Can you make at least one nine-letter word from those same letters? You may use any of the letters more than once.

## ✦ 322 ✦

Find the hidden phrase or title.

## ✦ 323 ✦

Find the hidden phrase or title.

## ✦ 324 ✦

One of the figures shown here lacks a characteristic common to the other five. Which figure is it, and why?

*Hint:* Don't consider symmetry.

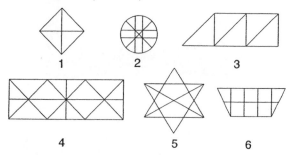

## ✦ 325 ✦

What follows is an argument: a premise and a conclusion based on that premise. See if you can determine whether the argument is valid or invalid.

If we are to survive and prosper as a species, solving the riddles of the universe via mathematics becomes the single most important focus of theoreticians. Thus, only the most brilliant minds will succeed.

## ✦ 326 ✦

Find the hidden phrase or title.

## ✦ 327 ✦

One glass is one-sixth full of blue liquid dye. Another glass, exactly the same size, is one-seventh full of the blue dye. Each glass is then filled to the top with water and their contents mixed together in a large container. What proportion of this final mixture is blue dye and what proportion is water?

## ✦ 328 ✦

A ten-letter word is hidden here. The last letter, R, is placed outside the grid of the other letters. Using each letter only once, and beginning with the first letter of the word, which may be in any of the nine positions of the grid, spell the word by moving up, down, sideways, or diagonally to adjacent letters.

## ✦ 329 ✦

In the following puzzle, the first number in each box has a certain relationship with the second number in that box. The relationships are the same for all four boxes. What is the missing number?

| 1 | 0 | | 3 | 26 | | 12 | 1,727 | | –2 | ? |

### ✦ 330 ✦

Find the hidden phrase or title.

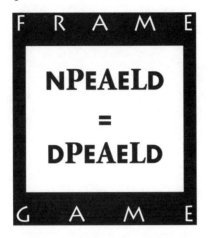

### ✦ 331 ✦

This next sequence puzzle is math related, but not exactly what you might think at first. Fill in the missing term.

*Hint 1:* Think leap year.

*Hint 2:* Be careful! Some calculators will give you the wrong answer.

$$0-3-4-4-8-2-\underline{\quad}$$

## ✦ 332 ✦

Here's a somewhat different perspective on the counting of stacked cubes. How many total cubes are there? Assume that all rows and columns are complete unless you actually see them end.

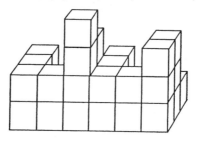

## ✦ 333 ✦

Four married couples live on a street in four different-colored houses. Given the information below, can you determine who is married to whom and the color of their house? (One of the houses is red.)

1. Harry does not live in the white house.
2. Alice is not married to Brad.
3. Steve lives in the yellow house.
4. John is not married to June.
5. Harry does not live in the blue house.
6. Alice lives in the blue house.
7. June is married to Harry.
8. Nancy is not married to Steve.
9. Sara is one of the wives.

### ✦ 334 ✦

Find the hidden phrase or title.

F R A M E

3:45 Friday
2:17 Monday
11:09 Thursday
6:56 Sunday

G A M E

### ✦ 335 ✦

All the words listed below share a common theme. What is it?

Timer
Spool
Reward
Emit
Diaper
Desserts

### ✦ 336 ✦

See if you can ascertain the nature of the relationship among the pictures in each row in order to fill in the missing figure in row 3.

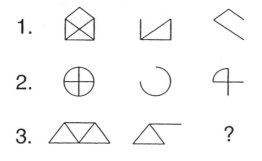

### ✦ 337 ✦

Find the hidden phrase or title.

## ✦ 338 ✦

I am six times as old as my sister. In one year I will be five times as old as my sister will be. In six years I will be three times as old as my sister will be. How old am I and how old is my sister?

## ✦ 339 ✦

The three words on the left have an interesting characteristic that is reversed with the three words on the right. Can you identify what that characteristic (and its reverse) is?

| | |
|---|---|
| **federal** | **defy** |
| **pond** | **hijack** |
| **ruts** | **calmness** |

## ✦ 340 ✦

Sometimes people wonder whether puzzles have any real-life applications. You be the judge. Here's an example:

A mother was throwing a birthday party for her daughter and realized that, with only nine scoops of ice cream, there wasn't enough to give two scoops to each of the five children present. She quickly came up with an idea that pleased all—and everyone got an equal amount of ice cream. By the way, she did not divide the scoops into fractional portions. How did this real-life mom solve her dilemma?

## ✦ 341 ✦

Find the hidden phrase or title.

## ✦ 342 ✦

You are playing a game with a friend called "penny pickup" in which nine pennies are placed on a table. In alternating turns, each player picks up at least one, but not more than five pennies per turn. The player who picks up the last penny wins. However, the penny has to be by itself for that player to win. In other words, if your opponent picks up five pennies, you can't pick up four and call yourself the winner. Under these guidelines, if you go first, is there a move you can make to ensure that you win?

## ✦ 343 ✦

Given the following letters and numbers, come up with the correct phrase:

**There are 24 K in P G.**

## ✦ 344 ✦

Here are five words. The first four are newly created English words that are related to their respective patterns. For the fifth pattern, you have to come up with the word; for the last word, you have to come up with the pattern.

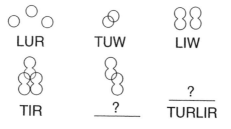

LUR          TUW          LIW

TIR          ?          TURLIR

## ✦ 345 ✦

At a convention of baseball trading card collectors, 30 dealers are interested in trading or selling their extra Mickey Mantle cards. Fifteen of the dealers have fewer than five such cards to trade, 11 others have more than six of them to trade, and three others have more than seven to trade or sell. What is the total number of dealers that have five, six, or seven Mickey Mantle cards?

## ✦ 346 ✦

What is the next letter in the following odd sequence?

**O−T−F−S−N−E−___**

## ✦ 347 ✦

Here is an *alphametic* (alphabet arithmetic problem): Fred, a football fanatic, is going to his first University of Nebraska football game. He doesn't know that Nebraska has the nation's longest streak of consecutive sellouts for their home games. See if you can find the number of people that were sitting in the north end zone with Fred. Each letter in the following alphametic retains the same value within the problem, and the value must be different from that of any other letter. Zero may not begin a word.

$$
\begin{array}{r}
\text{RED} \\
\text{RED} \\
\text{RED} \\
+\quad \text{FRED} \\
\hline
\text{HORDE}
\end{array}
$$

## ✦ 348 ✦

Here is a series challenge for the better brainteaser fan. Fill in the missing term in this mathematical series.

**9−73−241−561−1,081−1,849−?**

### ✦ 349 ✦

Find the hidden phrase or title.

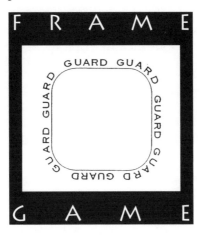

### ✦ 350 ✦

Bob was paddling his canoe upstream at a constant rate. After six miles, the wind blew his hat into the stream. Thinking that he had no chance to recover his hat, he continued upstream for six more miles before turning back. He continued rowing at the same rate on his return trip and overtook his hat at exactly the same spot where he began his journey, eight hours earlier. What was the velocity of the stream?

## ✦ 351 ✦

A zookeeper has to put 27 snakes in four cages. His problem is that he must have an odd number of snakes in each cage. How can he accomplish this? You can put any number of snakes in a cage as long as the total number of snakes in each cage is an odd number.

## ✦ 352 ✦

Given the following letters and numbers, see if you can come up with the correct phrase.

*Hint:* The phrase is not particularly common, but it's soluble. Think "game."

### 225 S on a S B

## ✦ 353 ✦

What is the fewest number of lines that would need to be erased to do away with all of the triangles in this figure?

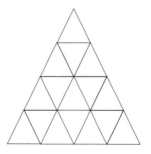

✦ **354** ✦

Find the hidden phrase or title.

✦ **355** ✦

A traveler at an airport had lots of time to kill between flights, so he decided to conduct an experiment on one of the moving walkways. He found he could walk the length of the walkway, moving in its forward direction, in one minute. Walking at the same rate *against* the forward direction of the walkway, it took him three minutes to cover the same distance. He wondered how long it would take him to cover one length if the walkway were to stop. Can you help him out? (This may not be as easy as it first appears.)

## ✦ 356 ✦

Find the hidden phrase or title.

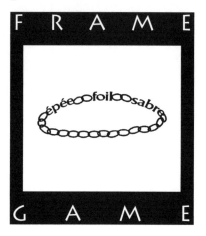

## ✦ 357 ✦

In five minutes, how many words can you make out of the word ***crazed*** (any number of letters allowed)?

## ✦ 358 ✦

What letter comes next in the following sequence?

*Hint:* Go straight to the answer.

**A–E–F–H–I–K–L–M–N–___**

### ✦ 359 ✦

Which one of the following patterns does not belong with the rest?

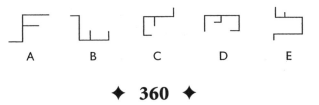

A          B          C          D          E

### ✦ 360 ✦

Using three nines, what is the largest number that can be created? You may use any mathematical symbols or signs you wish, with the exception of infinity (∞) and ellipses (…). You may not use the three nines together in combination, such as 99 × 9. In other words, each nine must remain by itself before any math operation is performed on it. Additionally, no mathematical symbol or sign may be used more than four times.

### ✦ 361 ✦

Unscramble the following:

**C I T U R S I U F T**

### ✦ 362 ✦

A box of candy can be divided equally among three, five, or thirteen people. What is the smallest number of pieces of candy the box can contain?

Find the hidden phrase or title.

♦ **364** ♦

Try your luck at this "trickle-down" puzzle. Remember, change one letter at a time to arrive at the answer.

**PULL**

——

——

——

**BITE**

### ✦ 365 ✦

What is the missing number in the following series?

*Hint:* Tackling this puzzle head-on won't help you. Try different directions.

**23 — 48 — 9 — 39 — ___ — 51 — 12 — 37**

### ✦ 366 ✦

The six words listed here share a common trait. What is it?

**pride — slime — grant — price — globe — whole**

### ✦ 367 ✦

What 9-letter word is written in the block below? Start with any letter and move one letter at a time, in any direction, but don't go back over any letter!

**O  N  N**
**C  U  D**
**M  U  R**

### ✦ 368 ✦

Unscramble these letters to make a word.

**YONNMSY**

## ✦ 369 ✦

Here is a list of scores from a fictitious college football season. Based on the given scores only, see if you can figure out who would win and by how much if Harvard were to play Montana during this season.

**Montana 27**
**Harvard 17**
**Notre Dame 14**
**New Hampshire 24**
**Ohio State 10**
**Connecticut 28**
**Maine 35**

**Notre Dame 13**
**New Hampshire 16**
**Ohio State 10**
**Connecticut 21**
**BYU 7**
**Maine 24**
**BYU 3**

## ✦ 370 ✦

The following is in code. Can you crack the code and decipher the message?

**JZF'CP LD JZFYR LD JZF QPPW**

## ✦ 371 ✦

Three dollar bills were exchanged for a certain number of nickels and the same number of dimes. How many nickels were there? Read this puzzle to a group of friends and see how long it takes to come up with the answer. You may be surprised!

✦ **372** ✦

Find the hidden phrase or title.

✦ **373** ✦

In the multiplication puzzles below, x, y, and z represents different digits. What is the sum of x, y, and z?

$$\begin{array}{r} yx \\ \times\ 7 \\ \hline zxx \end{array}$$

✦ **374** ✦

What is ½ of ⅔ of ⅗ of 240 divided by ½?

## ✦ 375 ✦

Alex, Ryan, and Steven are sports fans. Each has a different favorite sport among football, baseball, and basketball. Alex does not like basketball; Steven does not like basketball or baseball. Name each person's favorite sport.

## ✦ 376 ✦

Let's say 26 zips weigh as much as 4 crids and 2 wobs. Also, 8 zips and 2 crids have the same weight as 2 wobs. How many zips have the weight of 1 wob?

## ✦ 377 ✦

Find the hidden phrase or title.

**✦ 378 ✦**

There is a certain logic shared by the following four circles. Can you determine the missing number in the last circle?

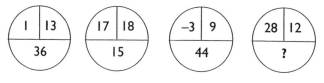

**✦ 379 ✦**

Find the hidden phrase or title.

**✦ 380 ✦**

Can you determine the next letter in the following series?

**A C F H K M ?**

## ✦ 381 ✦

The three words below can be rearranged into two words that are also three words! Can you decipher this curious puzzle?

**the red rows**

## ✦ 382 ✦

A friend has a bag containing two cherry gumdrops and one orange gumdrop. She offers to give you all the gumdrops you want if you can tell her the chances of drawing a cherry gumdrop on the first draw and the orange gumdrop on the second draw. Can you meet your friend's challenge?

## ✦ 383 ✦

One of the figures below lacks a common characteristic that the other five figures have. Which one is it and why?

*Hint:* This does not have to do with right angles or symmetry.

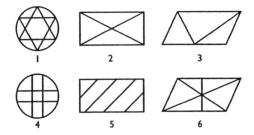

### ✦ 384 ✦

Find the hidden phrase or title.

### ✦ 385 ✦

A car travels from point A to point B (a distance of one mile) at 30 miles per hour. How fast would the car have to travel from point B to point C (also a distance of one mile) to average 60 miles per hour for the entire trip?

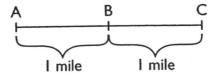

## ✦ 386 ✦

Try your luck at this "trickle-down" puzzle. Starting at the top, change one letter of each succeeding word to arrive at the word at the bottom.

**TOOK**

———

———

———

**BURN**

## ✦ 387 ✦

If the length of a rectangle is increased by 25 percent and its width is decreased by 25 percent, what is the percentage of change in its area?

## ✦ 388 ✦

The design on the left is made up of three paper squares of different sizes, one on top of the other. What is the minimum number of squares needed to create the design on the right?

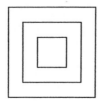

### ✦ 389 ✦

Here's a variation on an old classic. On what side of the line does the "R" go?

**A   B   D                    O   P   Q**
_____
**C   E   F   G   H   I   J   K   L   M   N**

### ✦ 390 ✦

Find the hidden phrase or title.

### ✦ 391 ✦

If I tripled one-quarter of a fraction and multiplied it by that fraction, I would get one-twelfth. What is the original fraction?

## ✦ 392 ✦

Given the initial letters of the missing words, complete this sentence.

### There are 100 Y in a C.

## ✦ 393 ✦

Two toy rockets are heading directly for each other. One is traveling at 50 miles per hour and the other is traveling at 70 miles per hour. How far apart will these two rockets be one minute before they collide?

## ✦ 394 ✦

Find the hidden phrase or title.

## ✦ 395 ✦

Think of five squares that are the same size. In how many ways can these five squares be combined, edge to edge? (No mirror images allowed.)

## ✦ 396 ✦

What number is four times one-third the number that is one-sixteenth less than three-thirty-seconds?

## ✦ 397 ✦

Below are five words. By adding the same three letters at the beginning of each word, you can come up with five new words. What three letters will do the trick?

**Her**

**Ion**

**Or**

**If**

**To**

## ✦ 398 ✦

A mixture of chemicals costs $40 per ton. It is composed of one type of chemical that costs $48 per ton and another type of chemical that costs $36 per ton. In what ratio were these chemicals mixed?

## ✦ 399 ✦

If $x^2$ is larger than 9, which of the following is true?

a. x is greater than 0.

b. 0 is greater than x.

c. x is equal to 0.

d. $x^3$ is greater than 0.

e. There is insufficient information to determine a solution.

## ✦ 400 ✦

What is 10 percent of 90 percent of 80 percent?

## ✦ 401 ✦

Find the hidden phrase or title.

## ✦ 402 ✦

Find the hidden phrase or title.

## ✦ 403 ✦

Based on the following information, how many pleezorns does Ahmad Adziz have?

Molly O'Brien has 22 pleezorns.

Debbie Reynolds has 28 pleezorns.

Roberto Montgomery has 34 pleezorns.

## ✦ 404 ✦

If the ratio of $5x$ to $4y$ is 7 to 8, what is the ratio of $10x$ to $14y$?

## ✦ 405 ✦

How many triangles of any size are in the figure below?

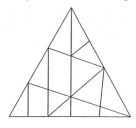

## ✦ 406 ✦

Decipher the following cryptogram:

**WLA'P XLJAP RLJO XGMXBSAE NSQLOS
PGSR GCPXG.**

## ✦ 407 ✦

How many four-letter words can you find in the word "twinkle"?
(Try for at least 15.)

## ✦ 408 ✦

Do this quickly: Write down twelve thousand twelve hundred
twenty-two.

## ✦ 409 ✦

Find the hidden phrase or title.

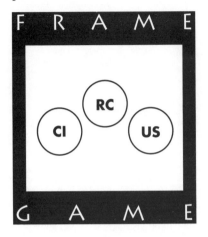

## ✦ 410 ✦

Below are four sets of letters that are related in a way known to virtually everyone. Can you find the missing two letters?

*Hint:* Some people have been known to take months to solve this!

ON
DJ
FM
AM
? ?

## ✦ 411 ✦

Find the hidden phrase or title.

## ✦ 412 ✦

In the strange land of Doubledown the alphabet appears to be hieroglyphics, but it isn't really much different from ours. Below is one of the Doubledown months spelled out. Which month of ours is comparable?

JOKE

## ✦ 413 ✦

Find the hidden phrase or title.

## ✦ 414 ✦

Quickly now, which is larger, $2^{67}$ or the sum of $2^{66} + 2^{65}$? How about $2^{67}$ or the sum of $2^{66} + 2^{66}$?

## ✦ 415 ✦

Unscramble this word:

**GORNSIMMAROCI**

## ✦ 416 ✦

Given the initial letters of the missing words, complete this sentence.

### There is one W on a U.

## ✦ 417 ✦

Below are six rays. Choosing two of the rays, how many angles of less than 90 degrees can you form? (Angle ACB is less than 90 degrees.)

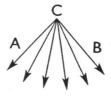

## ✦ 418 ✦

By arranging all nine integers in a certain order, it is possible to come up with fractions equal to ½, ⅓, ¼, ⅕, ⅙, ⅐, ⅛ and ⅑. See if you can come up with one of these.

Example: $\dfrac{1}{8} = \dfrac{3{,}187}{25{,}496}$

## ✦ 419 ✦

Find the hidden phrase or title.

## ✦ 420 ✦

What are the two missing numbers in the series below?

**8, 15, 10, 13, 12, 11, 14, 9, 16, 7, ?, ?**

## ✦ 421 ✦

Most of us know the following rules of divisibility:

A number is divisible by 2 if it ends in an even digit.

A number is divisible by 3 if the sum of its digits is divisible by 3.

Is there such a rule for dividing by 8?

## ✦ 422 ✦

What is the value of *z* in the following problem? (Each number is a positive integer between 0 and 9.)

## ✦ 423 ✦

Referring back to the last puzzle, where *z* was found to be 9, what is the value of *x*?

## ✦ 424 ✦

Which one of the following five words doesn't belong with the others, and why?

**Pail**
**Skillet**
**Knife**
**Suitcase**
**Doorbell**

## ✦ 425 ✦

If you wrote down all the numbers from 5 to 83, how many times would you write the number 4?

## ✦ 426 ✦

Four of the figures below share a characteristic that the fifth figure doesn't have. Can you determine which figure doesn't go with the others and why?

A          B          C          D          E

## ✦ 427 ✦

A certain barrel of candy can be equally divided (without cutting pieces) between five, seven, or thirteen people. What is the least number of pieces of candy the barrel could contain?

## ✦ 428 ✦

What is the value of the following?

$$\frac{1}{3 + \dfrac{1}{3\frac{1}{3}}}$$

### ✦ 429 ✦

Find the hidden phrase or title.

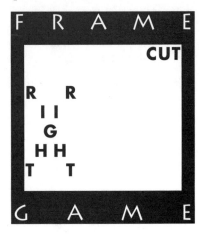

### ✦ 430 ✦

Which is greater, 107 percent of 300 or 50 percent of 600?

### ✦ 431 ✦

Imagine that a coin called a "kookla" is equal in value to either 7 gold pieces or 13 silver pieces. If you have 40 kooklas that you want to exchange for both silver and gold pieces and your bank has only 161 gold pieces on hand, how many silver pieces should you expect to receive with the 161 gold pieces?

## ✦ 432 ✦

Find the hidden phrase or title.

## ✦ 433 ✦

The diagram below can be drawn without lifting your pencil or crossing any other line. Can you do it?

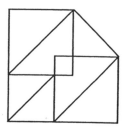

## ✦ 434 ✦

The diagram below is the beginning of a "magic square" in which all rows and columns and both diagonals add up to 34. Can you fill in the rest of the numbers?

| 1 | 8 | 13 | 12 |
|---|---|----|----|
| 14 |  |  |  |
| 4 |  | 16 |  |
| 15 |  |  |  |

## ✦ 435 ✦

The two numbers in each box have the same relationship to each other as do the two numbers in every other box. What is the missing number?

## ✦ 436 ✦

There are six chairs, each of a different color. In how many different ways can these six chairs be arranged in a straight line?

### ✦ 437 ✦

Find the hidden phrase or title.

### ✦ 438 ✦

Do the numbers 9 and 10 go above or below the line?

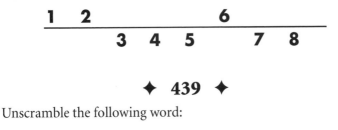

### ✦ 439 ✦

Unscramble the following word:

**RGAALEB**

## ✦ 440 ✦

Find the hidden phrase or title.

## ✦ 441 ✦

A concept that math students often find difficult to understand is that a negative multiplied by a negative results in a positive (example: –5 × –5 = 25). Can you come up with a real-life example, in words, to illustrate this?

## ✦ 442 ✦

Without using + or – signs, arrange five 8s so that they equal 9.

### ✦ 443 ✦

Find the hidden phrase or title.

### ✦ 444 ✦

How many individual cubes are in the configuration below? (All rows and columns run to completion unless you see them end.)

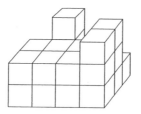

## ✦ 445 ✦

When the proper weights are assigned, this mobile is perfectly balanced. Can you determine the three missing weights?

*Hint:* Try starting with the 8-foot section of the mobile.

Remember that Distance × Weight = Distance × Weight.

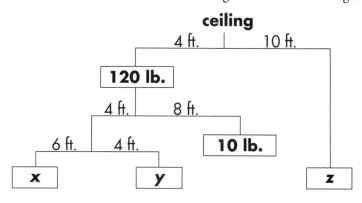

## ✦ 446 ✦

How many different words can you make from the word "Thanksgiving"? You might be surprised to find how many new words can be made from a word that doesn't contain the letter "e."

## ✦ 447 ✦

What is $\frac{1}{10}$ divided by $\frac{1}{2}$ divided by $\frac{1}{5}$ times $\frac{7}{9}$?

### ✦ 448 ✦

Below are two numbers represented by **x** and **y**. Regardless of the values of **x** and **y**, all possible answers resulting from the difference in these two numbers share one unique characteristic. What is it?

$$\begin{array}{r} \mathbf{xy} \\ -\mathbf{yx} \\ \hline \mathbf{??} \end{array}$$

### ✦ 449 ✦

The perimeter of a square has a value that is two-thirds of the number representing its square footage. What is the size of the square?

### ✦ 450 ✦

Find the hidden phrase or title.

## ✦ 451 ✦

Find the hidden phrase or title.

## ✦ 452 ✦

Here's another four-letter "trickle-down" puzzle. Find the three missing words, each with only one letter changed from the previous word, to arrive at **BARN**.

**MOOD**

———

———

———

**BARN**

## ✦ 453 ✦

In the game of craps, what are the chances that you will be a winner on your first roll by getting either a 7 or an 11?

## ✦ 454 ✦

What is the value of T in the following puzzle?

$$A + B = H$$
$$H + P = T$$
$$T + A = F$$
$$B + P + F = 30$$
$$A = 2$$

## ✦ 455 ✦

If five potatoes and six onions cost $1.22 and six potatoes and five onions cost $1.31, what does an onion cost?

## ✦ 456 ✦

You've been given $100 and told to buy 100 candles for a party. The first type of candle costs $0.50, the second $5.50, and the third $9.50. You must purchase exactly 100 candles and spend exactly $100. There is just one solution. How many candles of each type are purchased?

Find the hidden phrase or title.

## ✦ 458 ✦

Find the missing number in the following series:

$$\tfrac{5}{12} \quad \tfrac{1}{3} \quad \tfrac{1}{4} \quad \tfrac{1}{6} \quad \tfrac{1}{12} \quad ?$$

## ✦ 459 ✦

What is the first number having factors that add up to more than the number itself? (Don't include the number itself as one of the factors.)

## ✦ 460 ✦

Below are 10 matchsticks of equal length. By moving 2 and only 2 matchsticks, can you create 2 squares only, with no leftover matchsticks?

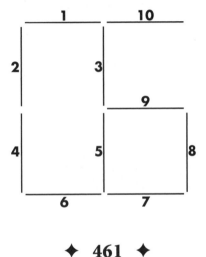

## ✦ 461 ✦

Given the initial letters of the missing words, complete this sentence:

### There are 206 B in the H B.

## ✦ 462 ✦

What number is ¼ of ⅓ of ⅙ of 432, divided by ⅓?

## ✦ 463 ✦

Find the hidden phrase or title.

## ✦ 464 ✦

One hundred people are applying for a sales position that would require them to sell both golf equipment and athletic shoes. Thirteen of the applicants have no prior experience in sales. Sixty-five of the applicants have previously sold golf equipment, and 78 of the applicants have sold athletic shoes. How many of the applicants have experience in selling both golf equipment and athletic shoes?

## ✦ 465 ✦

Find the hidden phrase or title.

## ✦ 466 ✦

What's the difference between 11 yards square and 11 square yards?

## ✦ 467 ✦

Find the four-letter word that will make new words when added in front of these:

**GUARD**
**LONG**
**TIME**

Find the hidden phrase or title.

## ✦ 469 ✦

What is the first year after the year 2000 in which the numbers of the year will read the same right-side-up and upside-down? What is the second year in which this will occur? (No fair using digital numerals, like ᒿ!)

## ✦ 470 ✦

H is to one as C is to six as N is to ?

### ✦ 471 ✦

Find the hidden phrase or title.

### ✦ 472 ✦

A "perfect" number is a number whose factors add up to the number (not including the number itself). For example:

The factors of 6 are 3, 2, and 1 and 3 + 2 + 1 = 6.

The factors of 28 are 14, 7, 4, 2, and 1 and 14 + 7 + 4 + 2 + 1 = 28.

What are the next two perfect numbers?

### ✦ 473 ✦

What are the chances of flipping a penny four times and getting at least two tails?

## ✦ 474 ✦

Find the hidden phrase or title.

## ✦ 475 ✦

Decipher the following cryptogram. Each letter represents another letter in the alphabet.

**OTD X GACOT ST BPWF WASFTOOX.**

## ✦ 476 ✦

How many times in a 12-hour period are the hands of a clock directly opposite each other?

## ✦ 477 ✦

A pipe can fill a swimming pool in three hours. A second pipe can fill the pool in two hours. If both pipes are turned on at the same time, how long will it take them to fill the pool?

## ✦ 478 ✦

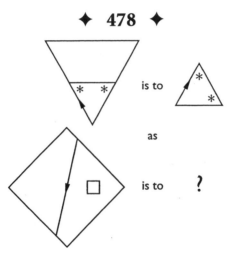

## ✦ 479 ✦

I am ten years older than my sister. There was a time when I was three times older than she was, and in one year I will be twice as old as she is. What is my age now?

## ✦ 480 ✦

Here's an interesting twist on an old series puzzle. See if you can come up with the missing letter.

*Hint:* This problem is best approached with an even hand.

**T    F    S    E    T    T    F    ?**

## ✦ 481 ✦

Find the hidden phrase or title.

## ✦ 482 ✦

Ten men and 8 women can shovel as much snow in 12 days as 8 men and 12 women can shovel in 10 days. Who are the better workers, men or women, and by how much?

## ✦ 483 ✦

Two of the following statements are false. What are the real names of each person?

**Susie's last name is Billingsley.**
**Susie's last name is Jenkins.**
**Sally's last name is Jenkins.**

## ✦ 484 ✦

If you find the correct starting point in the wheel below and move either clockwise or counterclockwise, the letters will spell out a common everyday word. What is the missing letter, and what is the word?

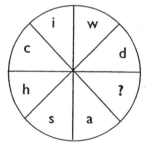

## ✦ 485 ✦

In a certain box of candy, the number of caramels is 25 percent of the number of other candies in the box. What percentage are the caramels of the entire box?

Find the hidden phrase or title.

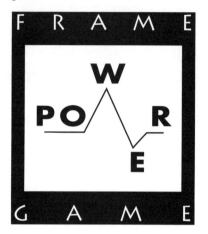

### ✦ 487 ✦

How many digits must be changed in the following addition problem to make the sum equal 245?

$$89$$
$$16$$
$$\underline{+98}$$

### ✦ 488 ✦

Find the hidden phrase or title.

### ✦ 489 ✦

Change one and only one letter in each successive word to come up with the next word:

**ROAD**

———

———

———

**LOOP**

## ✦ 490 ✦

Given the initial letters of the missing words, complete the following sentence.

*Hint:* Think of hydrogen.

### There are 106 E in the P T.

## ✦ 491 ✦

One of the following diagrams doesn't fit with the others. Which one is it? Why?

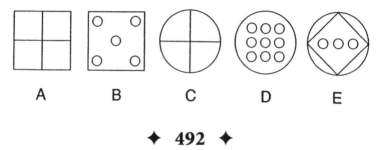

A          B          C          D          E

## ✦ 492 ✦

The starting lineup of a baseball team wants a photograph taken with all nine of the players sitting in a row on a bench. One of the ball players wonders how many different arrangements can be made of the order in which they sit. Do you know?

## ✦ 493 ✦

Here's fun with roman numerals. See if you can match column A to column B.

| | |
|---|---|
| $\overline{V}$ | 100 |
| $\overline{M}$ | 500 |
| $\overline{C}$ | 1,000 |
| C | 5,000 |
| $\overline{L}$ | 10,000 |
| $\overline{X}$ | 50,000 |
| $\overline{D}$ | 100,000 |
| D | 500,000 |
| M | 1,000,000 |

## ✦ 494 ✦

In a certain game, a ball can fall through any of 50 holes evenly spaced around a wheel. The chance that a ball would fall into any one particular hole is 1 in 50. What are the chances that 2 balls circling the wheel at the same time would fall into the same hole?

## ✦ 495 ✦

What is the missing number in the following series?

**84   12   2   ²/₅   ¹/₁₀   ?**

## ✦ 496 ✦

Find the hidden phrase or title.

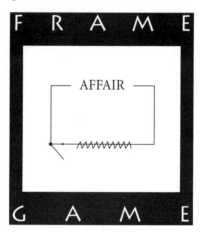

## ✦ 497 ✦

A man spent three-fourths of his money and then lost three-fourths of the remainder. He has $6 left. How much money did he start with?

## ✦ 498 ✦

Molly and Maggie are Martha's mother's son's wife's daughters. What relation is Martha to Molly and Maggie?

## ✦ 499 ✦

Find the hidden phrase or title.

## ✦ 500 ✦

In a foreign language, "rota mena lapy" means large apple tree, "rota firg" means small apple, and "mena mola" means large pineapple. Which word means tree?

## ✦ 501 ✦

Unscramble the following word:

**OMAHGOLR**

## ✦ 502 ✦

Find the hidden phrase or title.

## ✦ 503 ✦

See if you can determine a relationship among the following circles to find the missing number in the last circle.

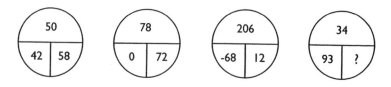

## ✦ 504 ✦

What is the missing number in the following series?

*Hint:* Could the numbers represent something other than quantities?

**13  9  14  4 — 2  5  14  4  9  14  ?**

## ✦ 505 ✦

Find the hidden phrase or title.

## ✦ 506 ✦

Given the initial letters of the missing words, complete this sentence:

### There are 180 D in a T.

## ✦ 507 ✦

What familiar four-letter word can be placed in front of each of the following to form four new words?

**Shelf**

**Worm**

**Mobile**

**Mark**

## ✦ 508 ✦

Four friends are going to a concert. When they arrive, there are only five seats together left in the theater. The manager will let all four friends in for free if one of them can tell her how many different seating arrangements are possible for four people with five empty seats. All four are let in free. Could you have given the correct answer?

## ✦ 509 ✦

What number is 4 times $\frac{1}{10}$ the number that is $\frac{1}{10}$ less than $\frac{3}{13}$?

## ✦ 510 ✦

Below is a teeter-totter with a 10-pound weight placed 10 feet to the left of the fulcrum and an 8-pound weight placed 5 feet to the left of the fulcrum. On the right side of the fulcrum is a 14-pound weight that needs to be placed in order to balance the weights on the left side. How many feet from the fulcrum should the 14-pound weight be placed?

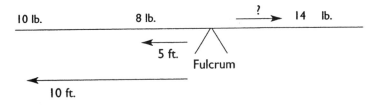

## ✦ 511 ✦

How many different squares (of any size) are in this figure?

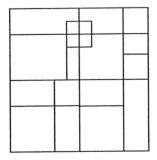

### ✦ 512 ✦

Find the hidden phrase or title.

### ✦ 513 ✦

Here's a series problem that may require a little extra patience…

**3 11 20 27 29 23 ?**

### ✦ 514 ✦

Unscramble this word:

**A T T R E S P N A R N**

### ✦ 515 ✦

The blank at the bottom of the second column below could be filled in by any one of three words. What are these words?

| EVIL | POST |
|------|------|
| LIVE | STOP |
| VILE | TOPS |
| VEIL | ____ |

### ✦ 516 ✦

Decipher the following cryptogram:

**SALTS LA ELLG**

### ✦ 517 ✦

Use three moves to get from the first word to the last.

**BIKE**
____
____
____
**MATH**

## ✦ 518 ✦

Find the hidden phrase or title.

## ✦ 519 ✦

A squash tournament has six rounds of single elimination for its singles competition. This includes the championship match, and there are no byes. How many players are entered when play begins?

## ✦ 520 ✦

If you built a four-sided pyramid—not counting the bottom as a side—using ping-pong balls, how many balls would be in a pyramid that had seven layers?

## ✦  521  ✦

When the proper weights are assigned, the mobile shown here is in perfect balance. What are the four missing weights?

*Hint*: distance × weight = distance × weight.

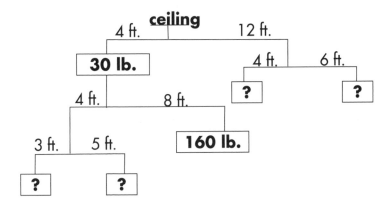

## ✦  522  ✦

What is the smallest number of square sheets of paper of any size that can be placed over each other to form the pattern below?

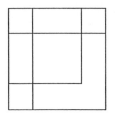

## ✦ 523 ✦

Given the initial letters of the missing words, complete the following sentence.

*Hint:* Think of Zorba.

### There are 24 L in the G A.

## ✦ 524 ✦

Find the hidden phrase or title.

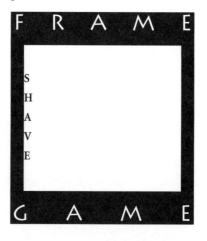

## ✦ 525 ✦

In a class of fewer than 30 students, two received a B on a math test, $\frac{1}{7}$ of the class received a C, $\frac{1}{2}$ received a D, and $\frac{1}{4}$ of the class failed the exam. How many students received an A?

# SOLUTIONS

**1.** $4^4 + 44 = 300$

**2.** It would appear in column B. Divide by 7 whatever number you wish to place, and see what the remainder is. If the remainder is 1, the number goes in column A; if the remainder is 2, the number goes in column B; and so on. (If the remainder is zero, however, the number goes in column G.)

**3.** Audrey will reach the destination first. Suppose they cover 12 miles, both walking at a rate of 2 miles per hour and running at a rate of 6 miles per hour. Use the formula $rt = d$ (rate × time = distance) to find each person's time.

Nancy (walks half the distance and runs half the distance):

$$2t = 6 \text{ mi., so } t = 3 \text{ hrs. walking}$$
$$6t = 6 \text{ mi., so } \underline{t = 1 \text{ hr. running}}$$
$$t = 4 \text{ hours total time}$$

Audrey (walks half the time and runs half the time):

$$2(\tfrac{1}{2}t) + 6(\tfrac{1}{2}t) = 12 \text{ mi.}$$
$$t + 3t = 12$$
$$4t = 12$$
$$t = 3 \text{ hours total time}$$

**4.** Each reads the same when held upside down.

**5.** Lead by example.

**6.** Simply add the sum of the two digits in any number to the sum of the two digits in the adjacent number to get the corresponding number in the row below. For example:

$$8 + 9 \ (89) \text{ and } 5 + 3 \ (53) = 25$$
$$5 + 3 \ (53) \text{ and } 1 + 7 \ (17) = 16$$

To find the missing number, add:

$$1 + 6 \ (16) \text{ and } 1 + 7 \ (17) = 15$$

**7.** His younger daughter received more—$4,000 more—than the older daughter. One way to solve this is to set up an equation that represents who received what:

$$x = \frac{1}{3}x + \frac{1}{5}x + \frac{1}{6}x + 9,000$$

$$x = \frac{10}{30}x + \frac{6}{30}x + \frac{5}{30}x + 9,000$$

$$x = \frac{21}{30}x + 9,000$$

Multiplying both sides of the equation by $\frac{30}{9}$, we get

$$\frac{30}{9}x = \frac{21}{9}x + \frac{270,000}{9}$$

$$\frac{30}{9}x - \frac{21}{9}x = 30,000$$

$$x = 30,000$$

Then

$$\frac{1}{3}x = \$10,000 \text{ (wife)}$$

$$\frac{1}{5}x = \$6,000 \text{ (son)}$$

$$\frac{1}{6}x = \$5,000 \text{ (older daughter)}$$

**8.** The missing number is 4. Simply add the first and second rows together to get the third row, like this:

$$
\begin{array}{r}
65{,}927 \\
+\ 14{,}354 \\
\hline
80{,}281
\end{array}
$$

**9.** If you know that 2:17 is the correct time, find the difference, positive or negative, of the other clocks:

| | | |
|---|---|---|
| clock 1 | 2:15 | −2 |
| clock 2 | 2:35 | +18 |
| clock 3 | 2:00 | −17 |
| clock 4 | 2:23 | +6 |
| clock 5 | 2:17 | 0 |
| 5 clocks | | 5 minutes |

As a group, the clocks average 1 minute fast.

**10.** The answer is $\frac{1}{12}$. If you convert each fraction to twelfths, the series looks like this:

$$\frac{8}{12}, \frac{7}{12}, \frac{6}{12}, \frac{5}{12}, \frac{4}{12}, \frac{3}{12}, \frac{2}{12}, \mathbf{\frac{1}{12}}$$

**11.** Cheaper by the dozen

**12.** Pages 6, 19, and 20 are also missing. Newspapers are printed double-sided, two pages to a sheet. The first and second pages are attached to the second-to-last and last pages—in this case, pages 23 and 24. The rest of the pages are attached as follows:

$$
\begin{array}{ll}
1\text{--}2 & \text{with } 23\text{--}24 \\
3\text{--}4 & \text{with } 21\text{--}22 \\
5\text{--}6 & \text{with } 19\text{--}20
\end{array}
$$

7–8    with 17–18
9–10   with 15–16
11–12  with 13–14

**13.** The value of $c$ is 14. To solve the problem, first set up the following equations:

$$(1)\ a + b = 13$$
$$(2)\ b + c = 22$$
$$(3)\ a + c = 19$$

Solve for b in equation (1):

$$b = 13 - a$$

Substitute this into equation (2):

$$13 - a + c = 22$$
$$-a + c = 9$$

Then combine equations (2) and (3) and solve for $c$:

$$-a + c = 9$$
$$\underline{a + c = 19}$$
$$2c = 28$$
$$c = 14$$

**14.** Rotate the first square 90 degrees to the right to obtain the second square.

| | X | |
|---|---|---|
| X | | |
| | | X |

**15.**
                                MOVE
                                MORE
                                MARE
                                BARE
                                BARK

**16.** Sarah is the second oldest; Liz is the oldest.

**17.** The missing number is 14. The first and last numbers added together make 19, as do the second number and the next-to-last number. Moving toward the middle in this fashion, each successive pair of numbers adds up to 19.

**18.** Broken promise

**19.** There are 23 triangles.

**20.** You are out of touch.

**21.** $2^{73}$ is larger by a long way.

**22.** e.  $\dfrac{1}{10\sqrt{10}}$

**23.** Carrot juice (The symbol before "juice" is called a "caret.")

**24.** The chances are 1 in 5. The possibilities are:

                        Blue$_1$, Blue$_2$
                        Blue$_1$, Green
                        Blue$_1$, Yellow
                        Blue$_2$, Green
                        Blue$_2$, Yellow

**25.** Yardstick

**26.** $17\frac{1}{3}$ lbs. Calculate the answer as follows:

$$1)\ A + B = 50\ \text{lbs}$$
$$\text{and 2)}\ \$8A + \$5B = 50 \times \$6$$

Then, multiply the first equation by –5, so:

$$-5A - 5B = -250$$

Next, combine with equation 2:

$$\$8A + \$5B = \$300$$
$$\underline{-5A - 5B = -250}$$
$$3A = 50$$
$$A = 17\frac{1}{3}\ \text{lbs.}$$

**27.** Place "end" at the beginning of each word:

> endear
> endless
> endanger

**28.** Your cup runneth over.

**29.** The correct answer is 20. Don't forget that the number 33 has two threes.

**30.** The answer is 3.

$$\tfrac{3}{4} \times \tfrac{1}{2} \times 16 = \tfrac{48}{8} = 6$$
$$\tfrac{1}{2} \times 6 = 3;\ 6 - 3 = 3$$

**31.** It will take 63 moves. For any number of discs $n$, the number of moves can be found by $2^n - 1$.

**32.** Here's a list of 15 words. Are they anywhere near the words you came up with?

serve
vice
rice
ice
see
seer
veer
sieve
eve
rise
ever
sever
cerise
rive
verse

**33.** The last number is 625. Subtract each individual digit in the numbers from 10 to crack the code.

**34.** A single discount of 12 percent is greater.

$$12\% \times 100 = 12.00$$
then
$$6\% \times 100 = 6.00$$
$$100 - 6 = 94$$
$$6\% \times 94 = 5.64$$
$$6.00 + 5.64 = 11.64$$
12.00 is greater than 11.64

**35.** Traffic congestion

**36.** The answer is zero!

**37.** YOU ARE A GENIUS. Move each of the letters in the puzzle back by three letters in the alphabet.

**38.** Draw a line from point 3 to point 12 and cut along the line to divide the figure. Turn the smaller figure upside down, then connect points 1 and 12 on the smaller figure with points 17 and 13, respectively, on the larger figure.

**39.** The next perfect number is 28 ($14 + 7 + 4 + 2 + 1 = 28$).

**40.** An upward turn in the economy

**41.** False. Some pibs may be rews, but it is not definite.

**42.** The first calculation is $\frac{1}{3} \times \frac{1}{3}$ of $12 \times 12$, or $\frac{1}{9}$ of 144, which equals 16. The second calculation is $(12 \div 3 \div 2)^3$, or $(\frac{4}{2})^3$, or 2 cubed, which is 8. The correct answer is the first calculation.

**43.** Milepost 900.

To solve this problem, recall that rate $\times$ time = distance. Let $x$ be the time it takes the *Seneca Streamer* to reach the milepost. Then:

$$60 \text{ mph} \times (x + 3) = 75 \text{ mph} \times x$$
$$60x + 180 = 75x$$
$$15x = 180$$
$$x = 12 \text{ hrs.}$$
$$75 \times 12 = 900 \text{ mi.}$$

**44.** The cyclist can take 96 ($4 \times 8 \times 3$) different routes.

**45.** Because there are two sides to the coin, the chances are always one in two.

**46.** The correct answer is (d). To solve this, we need to find

$$\frac{3/7}{4/9}$$

Invert the denominator and multiply:

$$3/7 \times 9/4 = 27/28$$

**47.** Making up for lost time

**48.** Place a decimal point between the two numbers to get 4.5.

**49.** The weight should be placed five feet from the fulcrum. First, calculate foot-pounds on the left side:

$$(5 \times 10) + (6 \times 5) = 80 \text{ ft.-lbs.}$$

The right side must equal the left side:

$$16x = 80$$
$$x = 5$$

**50.** There must be at least 66 chocolates—the least common denominator for 3, 6, and 11.

**51.**

P = horizontal
A = triangle
U = square
G = five
F = four
M = vertical

△ △ △ △ = PAF
MUFMAG = □
□
□
□
△
△
△
△
△

**52.** Overhead projector

**53.** It is 212 degrees Fahrenheit at which water boils.

**54.** The missing letter is S. Each letter is the first letter of the preceding number when spelled out.

**55.**

| | |
|---|---|
| 1. Unctuous | j. Oily |
| 2. Riparian | b. Relating to the bank of a lake or river |
| 3. Porcine | g. Relating to swine |
| 4. Plexus | c. An interlacing network |
| 5. Platitude | i. A trite remark |
| 6. Cosmology | a. Study of the universe |
| 7. Concatenation | h. A series connected by links |
| 8. Alacrity | f. Briskness |
| 9. Fecundate | e. Fertilize |
| 10. Newel | d. An upright post |

**56.** E. There is one more circle and one less straight line inside each figure than the number of sides to the figure—except for figure E. This eight-sided figure is the odd one out, because it contains only six straight lines and only eight circles.

**57.** I returned on Tuesday. The day before tomorrow is today, Friday. The day after that is Saturday, and four days before Saturday is Tuesday.

**58.** I look up to you.

**59.** 15 hours. The problem can be solved as follows:
$$7,500 - 150x = 4,500 + 50x$$
$$3,000 = 200x$$
$$x = 15$$

**60.** He is 32 years old. Here's the formula for the solution:
$$x + 4 = (x - 14) \times 2$$
$$x + 4 = 2x - 28$$
$$x = 32$$

**61.** D is the only figure that doesn't have a straight line dividing it in half.

**62.** The probability is 1 in 132,600.
$$\frac{1}{52} \times \frac{1}{51} \times \frac{1}{50} = \frac{1}{132,600}$$

**63.** Multiple personalities

**64.** It weighs approximately 1,700 pounds! One cubic foot of water weighs 62.4 pounds; one cubic yard (27 cubic feet) of water weighs 1,684.8 pounds.

**65.** It must win 90 percent of the games. This is probably best expressed as follows: If a team wins 60 percent of one-third of the games, it is the same as winning 20 percent of all the games. Therefore,

$$20x + \tfrac{2}{3}x = 80x$$
$$\tfrac{2}{3}x = 60x$$
$$2x = 180$$
$$x = 90$$

**66.** There are 50 stars on the United States flag.

**67.** It would be 4. The best way to solve this is by setting up proportions:

$$\frac{\tfrac{1}{2} \times 24}{8} = \frac{\tfrac{1}{3} \times 18}{x}$$
$$\tfrac{12}{8} = \tfrac{6}{x}$$
$$12x = 48$$
$$x = 4$$

**68.** Here's one way to solve the puzzle

> PART
> WART
> WANT
> WANE
> WINE

**69.** Upper crust

**70.** The answer is 1,234,321.

**71.** Growing concern

**72.** Six.

$$6m = b$$
$$8b = f$$
$$3f = y$$

We can find the number of bops in a yump by multiplying 8 × 3, or 24, and the number of murks in a yump by multiplying 24 times 6, or 144. So,

$$\frac{144 \text{ murks in a yump}}{24 \text{ bops in a yump}} = 6$$

**73.** It is 27 cubic yards—divide the number of cubic feet by 27 to get cubic yards.

**74.** The missing number is 448. In each triangle, multiply A times B and subtract 2 to get C.

**75.** A pear costs \$.05. Here's one way to solve the problem.
Letting $p$ = pears and $r$ = oranges, we have

$$(1)\quad 3p + 4r = 0.39$$
$$(2)\quad 4p + 3r = 0.38$$

Multiply equation (1) by 3 and equation (2) by $-4$:

$$9p + 12r = 1.17$$
$$\underline{-16p - 12r = -1.52}$$
$$-7p = -0.35$$

Now we can solve for $p$:

$$-7p = -.35$$
$$p = .05$$

**76.** 227. In each column, divide the top number by 3 to get the bottom number. Then, add 3 to the sum of the top and bottom numbers to get the middle number.

**77.** $\frac{1}{2}$ or $-\frac{1}{2}$

$$\frac{1}{5}x \times 4 \times x = \frac{1}{5}$$
$$\frac{4x^2}{5} = \frac{1}{5}$$
$$4x^2 = 1$$
$$x^2 = \frac{1}{4}$$
$$x = \frac{1}{2} \text{ or } -\frac{1}{2}$$

**78.** Think of it this way: If the leader receives twice as much as each of the others, that's the same as having seven members all earning the same amount, which would be $175 each. If the leader earns twice as much, he or she would therefore receive $350 per gig.

**79.** Double play

**80.** The missing number is 3. The numbers correspond to letters on the telephone keypad or dial.

**81.** Close encounters of the third kind

**82.** You would say *birta farn*. Notice that the adjectives follow the nouns.

$$klar = \text{red}$$
$$fol = \text{shine}$$
$$birta = \text{apples}$$
$$pirt = \text{bicycles}$$
$$farn = \text{big}$$
$$obirts = \text{often}$$

**83.** The numbers are 61, 62, and 63. To solve this, let $x$ be the first number; then $x + 1$ is the second number and $x + 2$ is the third number. An equation can be set up as follows:

$$x + (x + 2) = 124$$
$$2x + 2 = 124$$
$$2x = 122$$
$$x = 61$$

**84.** It equals 26. The midpoint between 20 and 32 is 26, and the midpoint between $16_a$ and $36_a$ is 26.

$$16_a = 20$$
$$\downarrow \qquad \downarrow$$
$$\text{Midpoint: } 26_a + 26$$
$$\uparrow \qquad \uparrow$$
$$36_a = 32$$

**85.** Over and over again

**86.** The word is "geometric."

**87.**

**88.** 80 people. When ¼ of the guests left, ¾ of the people remained. When ⅖ of them left, ⅗ of ¾ remained. When ¾ of the remaining people left, ¼ of ⅗ of ¾ remained (⁹⁄₈₀). Since 9 people were left at the end:

$$(¼ \times ⅗ \times ¾)x = 9$$
$$⁹⁄₈₀\, x = 9$$
$$x = 9 \times ⁸⁰⁄₉$$
$$x = 80$$

**89.** Blood is thicker than water.

**90.** 1,000—one thousand!

**91.** Stop in the name of love.

**92.** The probability is $(\frac{1}{2})^5$, or 1 in 32.

**93.** If you hold any of these letters up to a mirror; it will appear exactly the same as on the page.

**94.** $\frac{1}{3}$. In this series you take $\frac{1}{2}$ of the previous number, then $\frac{1}{3}$, $\frac{1}{4}$, $\frac{1}{5}$, and finally $\frac{1}{6}$. One-sixth of 2 equals $\frac{2}{6}$, or $\frac{1}{3}$.

**95.** Statement (2) is true.

**96.** Six is the maximum number of lines.

**97.** A bird in the hand is worth two in the bush.

**98.** The missing number is 14. Pick any piece of the pie and look directly opposite that piece: the larger of the two numbers is 3 times the smaller number minus 1.

**99.**

FAST
FIST
MIST
MINT
MIND

**100.** Eight of the one-inch cubes have three blue sides—they were the corners of the four-inch cube.

**101.** The case costs $5; the binoculars cost $95. To solve this, let $b$ = the binoculars and $c$ = the case:

$$b + c = 100$$
$$b = 90 + c$$

Now substitute:

$$90 + c + c = 100$$
$$90 + 2c = 100$$
$$2c = 10$$
$$c = 5$$

**102.** It will take ten seconds. Because the first strike sounds at zero seconds, two strikes sound in one second, three strikes in two, etc.

**103.** Two eggs over easy

**104.** Sammy must be a girl.

**105.** I'd rather be in Philadelphia.

— W. C. Fields

**106.** There are nine innings in a baseball game.

**107.** MAD

**108.** There are 17 squares.

**109.** High hurdles

SOLUTIONS

**110.** It might look something like this:

1, 2, 3, 4, 5, 6, 7, 8, 9, ✧, ☆, ✶, 10

(Almost any symbols could be used to represent the old numbers 10, 11, and 12.) Our old number 13 now becomes 10. If you choose to call this number 10, the new symbols would need new names, as would all the numbers that contain these two symbols.

**111.** Frequency is measured in hertz.

**112.** Home stretch

**113.** Parliamentary

**114.** The missing letter is R. Starting with the W in the first circle and moving counterclockwise in each successive circle, the words "What is the letter" are spelled out.

**115.** CMXLIV

**116.** 2,047

**117.** The pursuit of happiness

**118.** Your odds are 2 to 3:

$$\text{Odds in favor of an event} = \frac{\text{Probability of favorable event}}{\text{Probability of unfavorable event}}$$

$$\frac{^2/_5}{^3/_5} = \frac{2}{3}$$

**119.** Head

**120.** Arc de Triomphe

**121.** The second number in each box is the first number cubed plus three, so the missing number is 30.

**122.** Bach. B-sharp and C are the same note.

**123.** There are 42 triangles.

**124.** He went under the knife.

**125.** 1–b, 2–e, 3–a, 4–c, 5–f, 6–g, 7–d

**126.** Here are 15. Can you come up with more?

| | |
|---|---|
| burn | numb |
| bun | sum |
| run | nub |
| sun | um |
| runs | men |
| rum | muse |
| use | ruse |
| user | |

**127.** 3, 2. The numbers are arranged in alphabetical order.

**128.** All worked up

**129.** There are six points on the Star of David.

**130.** H is the only figure that is pointing counterclockwise.

**131.** Be on time.

**132.** $Z = -7$

| 12 | | 18 | | 26 | | 38 | | 49 |
|---|---|---|---|---|---|---|---|---|
| | 6 | | 8 | | 12 | | 11 | |
| | | 2 | | 4 | | $-1$ | | |
| | | | 2 | | $-5$ | | | |
| | | | | $-7$ | | | | |

The number in each row is found by subtracting the first of the two numbers above it from the second.

**133.**
> FEAR
> DEAR
> DEER
> DEEP
> KEEP

**134.** The answer is 72. The series goes like this:
$$1^2 - 1, 2^2 + 2, 3^2 - 3, 4^2 + 4, 5^2 - 5, 6^2 + 6, 7^2 - 7, 8^2 + 8, 9^2 - 9, \text{etc.}$$

**135.** A diamond in the rough

**136.** Phase (b) and (d) are equivalent. "Fourteen yards square" describes a square measuring 14 yards by 14 yards, or 196 square yards.

**137.** There are 360 degrees in a square.

**138.** Knocked for a loop

**139.** Celestial

**140.** Odds and ends

**141.**
madam
level
civic
radar
repaper
deified
rotator
(and there are more)

**142.** You are the caddy, and your fee has probably just increased considerably.

**143.** Here's one way:

MEAL
MEAT
MOAT
BOAT
BOOT
BOOK

**144.** Turn the other cheek.

**145.** It is 7:00 P.M.

Let $x$ = the time it is now, and $y$ = the time until midnight

$$x + 4 = 12 - y$$
and
$$x + 3 = 12 - 2y$$

Subtracting the second equation from the first, we get

$$1 = y$$
Then,
$$x + 4 = 11$$
$$x = 7$$

**146.** There are nine positions on a baseball team.

**147.** One possible answer: Shown below are the two original squares and a shaded square created by placing matchsticks 4 and 5 in the middle of each original square.

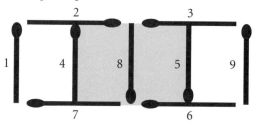

**148.** 8. Starting at both ends and working toward the middle, each pair of numbers adds up to 52.

**149.** The prefix is **sub-**.

**150.** Goldie is Nancy's aunt.

**151.** Pig latin

**152.** If rounded up, the missing number is 6. The series (with a decimal point before the zero) represents the fraction $\frac{1}{14}$ expressed in decimal form.

**153.** 8. Set up a proportion to solve this puzzle: letting $x$ be the unknown number,

$$\frac{48}{2} \text{ is to 32 as } \frac{18}{3} \text{ is to } x$$

$$24 \text{ is to 32 as 6 is to } x$$

$$3 \text{ is to 4 as 6 is to } x$$

$$\frac{3}{4} = \frac{6}{x}$$

$$3x = 24$$

$$x = 8$$

**154.** Three-point shot

**155.** Here's one way:

```
S     T     R     A     I     N

   T     R     A     I     N

      R     A     I     N

         R     A     N

            A     N

               A
```

**156.** 24

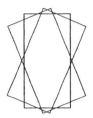

**157.** 1 out of 2. There are $2^3 = 8$ possible combinations when throwing a penny three times. Each combination has a $\frac{1}{8}$ probability, and four of them involve at least two heads:

$$
\begin{array}{ll}
\text{HHH} & \frac{1}{8} \\
\text{HTT} & \\
\text{TTT} & \\
\text{THH} & \frac{1}{8} \\
\text{HHT} & \frac{1}{8} \\
\text{HTH} & \frac{1}{8} \\
\text{THT} & \\
\text{TTH} &
\end{array}
$$

**158.** 50 and 40. Let $x$ be the first number and $y$ be the second number. From the statement of the problem we get:

$$x - y = 10 \ (1)$$
$$xy = 2{,}000 \ (2)$$

From Eq. (2) we get $x = \dfrac{2{,}000}{y}$. Substituting that value in Eq. (1) gives:

$$\frac{2{,}000}{y} - y = 10$$

$$2,000 - y^2 = 10y$$
$$-y^2 + 2,000 + 10y = 0$$
$$y^2 - 2,000 - 10y = 0$$
$$(y - 40) \times (y + 50) = 0$$

Therefore, we want the positive values for the above and they are 50 and 40.

**159.** Nobel Prize

**160.** 1,000,000 seconds is 11.57 days.

**161.** None. Instead, turn the puzzle upside down!

$$
\begin{array}{r}
18 \\
66 \\
+89 \\
\hline
173
\end{array}
$$

**162.** PSV

**163.** BRAINTEASER

**164.** 1278. Each of the code numbers can be found by subtracting the original number from 2,000.

**165.** 1

$$84 \times \tfrac{3}{7} = 36$$
$$36 \times \tfrac{2}{9} = 8$$
$$8 \times \tfrac{1}{4} = 2$$
$$2 \times \tfrac{1}{2} = 1$$

**166.** $2^{(n+1)} - 2$

**167.** 61 and 91, respectively. Can you determine the pattern for any perfect cube, using integers only?

$$27 - 19 = 8 = 2^3$$
$$64 - 37 = 27 = 3^3$$
$$125 - x = 4^3$$
$$x = 125 - 64 = 61$$
$$216 - y = 5^3$$
$$y = 216 - 125 = 91$$

**168.** The two figures in the first part of the analogy merge into one figure. When the squares merge, they turn into a circle. When the circles merge, they disappear. Circles and squares that don't merge stay as they are.

**169.** $\frac{4}{10}$. This is actually two series within one:

Starting with $\frac{1}{7}$ and looking at every other fraction, one series is $\frac{1}{7}, \frac{2}{8}, \frac{3}{9}, \frac{4}{10}$.

The other series starts with $\frac{4}{9}$ and goes on to $\frac{5}{10}$ and $\frac{6}{11}$.

**170.** There are two pints in a quart.

**171.** Too little, too late

**172.** Adam Mammale is not human.

**173.** COMPLETED

**174.** Clams on the half-shell

**175.** Here's one way:

> PARTY
> PARTS
> DARTS
> DARES
> DANES
> DUNES

**176.** Lickety-split

**177.** The letters arrayed around the triangles spell out:

> IT IS HIGH NOON
>
> The number, therefore, is 12.

**178.** 15.12. Each successive number is found by taking the percentage of the previous number, starting with 100%, then 90%, 80%, 70%, etc.:

$$
\begin{array}{rcl}
100 \times 100\% &=& 100 \\
100 \times 90\% &=& 90 \\
90 \times 80\% &=& 72 \\
72 \times 70\% &=& 50.4 \\
50.4 \times 60\% &=& 30.24 \\
30.24 \times 50\% &=& 15.12
\end{array}
$$

**179.** A secret between friends

**180.** "Singing in the Rain"

**181.** Here is one solution:

$$\frac{3}{6} = \frac{9}{18} = \frac{27}{54}$$

There is another solution. Can you find it?

**182.** Prima donna

**183.**

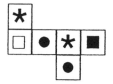

**184.** Quarterback

**185.** Either third or fourth.

**186.** 27,000. The repeating pattern is, respectively, 2, 3, and 5 times the preceding number.

**187.** Joseph could be my grandson.

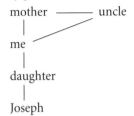

```
mother ——————— uncle
   |                  /
   me ——————————————/
   |
daughter
   |
Joseph
```

**188.** We confess, we only found 24. Did you find more?

| | | | |
|---|---|---|---|
| con | nose | nice | ice |
| son | on | sine | nine |
| soon | sin | fine | fie |
| noon | fin | since | noose |
| no | scion | one | none |
| scone | noise | ion | cone |

**189.** 55. Here is a proportion that solves this puzzle (where $x$ is the unknown number of baseballs):

$$\frac{30}{9 \times 2} = \frac{x}{11 \times 3}$$

$$\frac{5}{3} = \frac{x}{33}$$

$$3x = 165$$

$$x = 55$$

**190.** Stepbrothers

**191.** Carrots. A carrot is a vegetable, whereas the others are classified as fruits.

**192.** D

**193.** Pete has $8/35$ of the candy. Here's how to get the answer:

After Joe takes $3/5$ of the candy, $2/5$ of the bag is left. If we let Pete's share be $x$ and Bob's share be $3/4x$, we have

$$x + 3/4x = 2/5$$
$$7/4x = 2/5$$
$$x = 2/5 \times 4/7$$
$$x = 8/35$$

Thus, Pete has $8/35$ of the candy and Bob has $6/35$ of the candy.

**194.** F = 23. Substituting Eq. (1) in Eq. (2), gives

$$A + B + P = T$$

And substituting Eq. (5) in this last equation gives

$$8 + B + P = T \qquad (6)$$

If we then substitute Eq. (3) in Eq. (4), we get

$$B + P + T + A = 30$$

Substituting Eq. (5) in this last equation gives

$$22 - B - P = T \qquad (7)$$

Adding Eqs. (6) and (7) gives the following:

$$8 + B + P = T$$
$$22 - B - P = T$$
$$30 = 2T$$
$$\text{So, } T = 15 \qquad (8)$$

Substituting Eqs. (5) and (8) in Eq. (3) gives

$$F = 15 + 8 = 23$$

**195.**    1) CAGI

2)

The breakdown of the relationships:

D = Horizontal

C = Vertical

A = ○

E = ◇

G = 3

B = 2

Y = Uncoupled
I = Coupled

**196.** The order should be 4, 1, 3, 5, 2.

**197.** One possible answer:

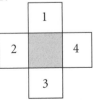

**198.** Ser

**199.** 168. The pattern behind this sequence can be revealed by factoring the individual terms:

$$5 = 2^2 + 1$$
$$8 = 3^2 - 1$$
$$26 = 5^2 + 1$$
$$48 = 7^2 - 1$$
$$122 = 11^2 + 1$$

This shows that the squares of the prime numbers are involved. So the next term in the sequence must be

$$13^2 = 169$$
$$169 - 1 = 168$$

**200.** Getting it all together

**201.** Bleary. Take the last three letters of each pair of words to form the new words.

**202.** MCDXLIX

**203.** It should be placed 16 ft to the right of the fulcrum.

Left side: Currently there is a total of

20 ft $\times$ 40 lb + 10 ft $\times$ 20 lb = 800 + 200 = 1,000 ft-lb

Right side: Currently there is 10 ft $\times$ 60 lb = 600 ft-lb. Since this is less than what's on the left side, the 25-lb weight must go somewhere on the right side. Let's call the exact distance from the fulcrum $y$:

$$10 \times 60 + 25y = 1,000$$
$$25y = 400$$
$$y = 400/25 = 16 \text{ ft}$$

**204.** A bad spell of flu

**205.** $1\frac{1}{2}$

**206.** 21%. If you were to pick a student at random, the probability that he or she was taking at least one of the courses is 64% + 22% – 7% = 79%, which means there is a 21% chance that the student was taking neither course.

**207.** A = 1, B = 3, C = 2. We can arrive at the answer via a plan of attack that examines the rules one at a time to chart the possibilities:

Rule (a): This tells us too little at this point.

Rule (b): This raises two clear possibilities:

$$B = 2, A = 3, C = 1$$
or
$$B = 1, A = 3, C = 2$$

Let's assume one of these is correct and look at the next two rules.

Rule (c): This eliminates possibility (1).

Rule (d): This eliminates possibility (2). But what if C = 3 while B = 1 or 2? That raises the following two possibilities:

$$B = 2, A = 1, C = 3$$
or
$$B = 1, A = 2, C = 3$$

Rule (e): This eliminates possibilities (3) and (4). Thus, B is not 1 or 2 and so it must be 3.

Rule (f): If B = 3, then A, not being 2, must be 1. And C, therefore, must be 2.

**208.** There are six outs in an inning.

**209.** Here's one way:

> TIMER
> TIMES
> DIMES
> DINES
> DUNES
> DUNKS

**210.** "All Things Great and Small"

**211.** The glass is $^5/_{16}$ empty. The $^5/_8$ is equal to $^{10}/_{16}$, which means that if the glass were $^{10}/_{16}$ full, you would have emptied $^6/_{16}$ of it. You empty $^5/_{16}$ of the glass first.

**212.** 125. 5 is 25 times $^1/_5$; likewise, 125 is 25 times 5.

**213.** British Open

**214.** D. Beginning with the S at the top of the first triangle and moving counterclockwise, the letters spell out STRETCH YOUR MIND.

**215.** Check-kiting

**216.** She is their aunt.

**217.** Eleven. Tom had to win four matches to draw even with Bill, and then Tom had to win three more times:

$$4 + 4 + 3 = 11$$

**218.** Ants in his pants

**219.** 52%. First, we express the given fractions in terms of the least common denominator. Thus,

$$\frac{1}{7} = \frac{11}{77} \text{ and } \frac{3}{11} = \frac{21}{77}$$

Now we can restate the question as

"$\frac{11}{77}$ is what percent of $\frac{21}{77}$ ?"

This is the same as "11 is what percent of 21?"

And $\frac{11}{21} = 52\%$ (approximately).

**220.** Here's one way to solve this:

$$\frac{8888}{88} = 101; \quad 101 - \frac{8}{8} = 100$$

**221.** Here are three. Can you find more?

aardvark

mascara

anagram

**222.** "Star Wars"

**223.** Zero. The fisherman caught 3, 6, 9, and 12 fish on the second, third, fourth, and fifth days, respectively. If we let $x$ represent the number of fish caught on the first day, then

$$x + (x + 3) + (x + 6) + (x + 9) + (x + 12) = 30$$
$$x + x + 3 + x + 6 + x + 9 + x + 12 = 30$$
$$5x + 30 = 30$$
$$5x = 0$$
$$x = 0$$

**224.** 151. In each column, divide the top number by 3 to get the bottom number. Then add 3 to the sum of the top and bottom numbers to get the middle number.

**225.** 86,400 seconds in a day

**226.** SCRABBLE

**227.** 24

**228.** 321. Divide 3 into 960 and add 1 (for the first term in the sequence).

**229.**

$$
\begin{array}{r}
15 \\
\times 35 \\
\hline
75 \\
45 \\
\hline
525
\end{array}
$$

**230.** Pace back and forth

**231.** The amateur's mother

**232.** Because your chances of winning are 1 in 9. The probability of rolling a 2 is $\frac{1}{36}$; of a 3 is $\frac{2}{36}$; and of a 12 is $\frac{1}{36}$. And $\frac{1}{36} + \frac{2}{36} + \frac{1}{36} = \frac{4}{36} = \frac{1}{9}$. Thank your friend and buy him a drink.

**233.**

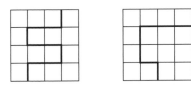

**234.** Tocopherol is vitamin E. All the rest are minerals.

**235.**    $\dfrac{1}{2\sqrt{3}}$    or    $\dfrac{\sqrt{3}}{6}$

Let the original fraction be $\dfrac{1}{x}$:

$$\frac{1}{x} \times \frac{4}{5} \times \frac{1}{x} = \frac{4}{5x^2}$$

$$\frac{4}{5x^2} = \frac{1}{15}$$

$$5x^2 = 60$$

$$x^2 = 12$$

$$x = \sqrt{12}$$

$$x = \sqrt{4 \times 3}$$

$$x = 2\sqrt{3}$$

$$\text{Ans.} = \frac{1}{2\sqrt{3}} \quad \text{or} \quad \frac{\sqrt{3}}{6}$$

SOLUTIONS

**236.** Reverse the charges.

**237.** Let $x$ = number of $0.50 candles, $y$ = the number of $5.50 candles, and $z$ = the number of $9.50 candles. From the problem statement we know that

$$x + y + z = 100 \qquad (1)$$
$$0.50x + 5.50y + 9.50z = 100 \qquad (2)$$

We can now multiply Eq. (1) by $-0.5$ and add it to Eq. (2):

$$-0.5x - 0.5y - 0.5z = -50$$
$$+0.5x + 5.5y + 9.5z = +100$$

Thus,

$$5y = 50 - 9z$$
$$y = 10 - \frac{9}{5}z$$

Since we're dealing with whole numbers, $z$ must be a whole number and a multiple of 5. In this case, $z$ can equal only 5, because with any greater number $y$ would become negative.

So

$z = 5$, $y = 1$ and thus $x$ must be 94 candles at $.50 each.

**238.**
$$26^2 = 676$$
$$101^2 = 10,201$$

**239.** 30. Triangles ABC, ABE, ABH, ABI, ACD, ACE, ACH, ADH, AEF, AFG, AFH, AGH, AHI, BCD, BCH, BCI, BDH, BEH, BGH, CEF, CEH, CEJ, CFH, CFJ, CHI, DGH, EFH, EHJ, FHI, and FHJ

**240.** The odd one out

**241.** J. These are the first letters of the months of the year, starting with December and running backward.

**242.**     $A = 1$     $B = 8$     $C = 9$
            $D = 3$     $E = 4$     $F = 6$
            Thus, $1 \times 8 \times 9 = 72 = 3 \times 4 \times 6$.

**243.** Here's one. Can you find others?

> post
> spot
> tops
> pots
> opts

**244.** 30 beasts and 15 birds. Let $b$ be the number of beasts and $B$ be the number of birds. From the total number of feet, we know that

$$B(2 \text{ feet/bird}) + b(4 \text{ feet/beast}) = 150, \text{ or}$$
$$2B + 4b = 150$$

The total number of creatures is $B + b = 45$,
$$\text{so } B = 45 - b$$

Now we can substitute this last equation into the feet equation:

$$2(45 - b) + 4b = 150$$
$$90 - 2b + 4b = 150$$
$$2b = 60$$

$b = 30$ beasts and $B = 45 - 30 = 15$ birds

**245.** ⅓. The relationship between successive numbers, beginning with the first 240, is:

$$1, \tfrac{1}{2}, \tfrac{1}{3}, \tfrac{1}{4}, \tfrac{1}{5} \text{ and } \tfrac{1}{6}.$$
$$\tfrac{1}{6} \times 2 = \tfrac{1}{3}$$

**246.** 50. Compare the two equations as presented in this diagram:

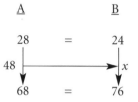

As you can see from the diagram, 48 is the midpoint between 28 and 68. We now need to find the midpoint between 24 and 76. We do this by adding 24 and 76, which equals 100, and dividing that by 2. Therefore, the answer is 50.

**247.** 90°

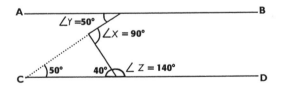

**248.** The word is PUZZLES. The answer can be obtained by putting each letter of the alphabet in a 5 x 5 grid, with *Y* and *Z* sharing the last box. The two-digit numbers are decoded by making the row number the tens digit and the column number the units digit of the letter being sought. Thus, for example, the code 41 represents row 4, column 1, which is the letter P.

*Note:* It was the ancient Greek historian Polybius who first proposed a similar method of substituting numbers for letters.

|   | 1 | 2 | 3 | 4 | 5 |
|---|---|---|---|---|---|
| 1 | A | B | C | D | E |
| 2 | F | G | H | I | J |
| 3 | K | L | M | N | O |
| 4 | P | Q | R | S | T |
| 5 | U | V | W | X | Y/Z |

**249.** 76 trombones in the big parade

**250.** The figures correspond to each other as follows: A to E, B to F, C to G, and D to H. Blank squares in Figures A through D are filled with Xs in corresponding Figures E through H. Filled squares in Figures A through D are made blank. The correct figure is shown below.

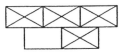

**251.** Only one doctor is a dermatologist. The other 99 are, of course, surgeons.

**252.** Each of the words can be made into at least two other words:

| | |
|---|---|
| rifle: | flier, lifer |
| evil: | live, vile (and veil) |
| deal: | lead, dale |
| rats: | star, arts (and tars) |
| tale: | late, teal |

**253.** B

**254.** $93.26

$$
\begin{array}{r}
2442 \\
5442 \\
\underline{1442} \\
93.26
\end{array}
$$

**255.** 1. The first nine numbers of this sequence will repeat to infinity when the consecutive integers from 1 to 9 are squared and the resultant digits added together until a one-digit number is achieved:

$$1^2 = 1$$
$$2^2 = 4$$
$$3^2 = 9$$
$$4^2 = 16, \text{ and } 1 + 6 = 7$$
$$5^2 = 25, \text{ and } 2 + 5 = 7$$
$$6^2 = 36, \text{ and } 3 + 6 = 9$$
$$7^2 = 49, \text{ and } 4 + 9 = 13 \text{ and } 1 + 3 = 4$$
$$8^2 = 64, \text{ and } 6 + 4 = 10 \text{ and } 1 + 0 = 1$$
$$9^2 = 81, \text{ and } 8 + 1 = 9$$
$$10^2 = 100, \text{ and } 1 + 0 = 1$$

**256.** There are fifty-four external sides (the number of faces on nine cubes). Since two gallons are needed to paint one cube, you would need 2 x 9, or 18 gallons of paint to cover the figure.

**257.** Line up in single file

**258.** The value of R is 20. Because it is known that Q + M = C, it follows that Q + M + K = R. We also know that R + Q = S, so in the equation M + K + S = 40, we can replace S with R + Q. The equation then becomes M + K + R + Q = 40, or M + K + R = 32 because Q is 8. Rearranging the equations to solve for R, we then have:

$$8 + M + K = R$$
$$32 - M - K = R$$

$$40 = 2R \text{ and therefore } R = 20$$
$$\text{Because } R + Q = S$$
$$20 + 8 = S$$
$$S = 28$$

**259.** Tomorrow is another day.

**260.**   $\dfrac{4!}{\sqrt{4}} = \dfrac{4 \times 3 \times 2 \times 1}{2} = 12$

**261.** The missing number is 259. Starting with 1, the sequence is follows:

$$1^2, 2^2 + 1, 3^2 + 2, 4^2 + 3 \text{ (first circle)}$$
$$1^3, 2^3 + 1, 3^3 + 2, 4^3 + 3 \text{ (second circle)}$$
$$1^4, 2^4 + 1, 3^4 + 2, 4^4 + 3 \text{ (third circle)}$$

**262.** Crime wave

**263.**

These are the numbers 1, 3, 5, 7, 9, and 11, back to back with their reverse images.

**264.** ½ lb. The ⅕ lb of chocolate is equivalent to ⅖ of a block of chocolate. Multiply the ⅕ lb by 5⁄2 to find the weight of the whole block:

$$1/5 \times 5/2 = 5/10 = 1/2 \text{ lb}$$

**265.** Fight breaking out (or fighting across the border)

**266.** His wife bets the opposite of whatever her husband bets, usually double or triple the amount that he has placed.

**267.**

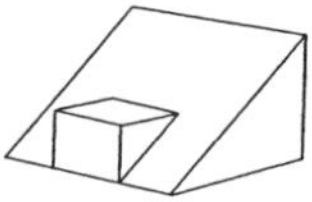

**268.** $\frac{2}{1}$.

These are the ratios of the frequencies of the eight notes of the diatonic scale, beginning with C. They are usually written

$$\frac{1}{1}:\frac{9}{8}:\frac{5}{4}:\frac{4}{3}: \text{etc.}$$

**269.** LATITUDE

**270.** 5:00 A.M.

**271.** A piece of the pie

**272.** D

**273.** There's a fine line between love and hate.

**274.** You bet it makes a difference! If $\frac{1}{30}$ were the true mean of $\frac{1}{40}$ and $\frac{1}{20}$, then neither dealer would have an advantage. However, the mean of $\frac{1}{40}$ and $\frac{1}{20}$ is 0.0375. The fraction $\frac{1}{30}$ is equivalent to 0.0333! So the buyers at the store across the street are being taken to the cleaners. The average of the reciprocals of two numbers is not the same as the reciprocal of the average.

**275.** No room for error

**276.** BAR

**277.** If you had three quarters, four dimes, and four pennies, which totals $1.19, you couldn't make change for a dollar.

**278.** Name

**279.** 7, 0. If you take the difference between each of the numbers, respecting whether that difference is positive or negative, you will find the following pattern:

$$3, 3, -7, 3, 3, -7, 3 \ldots$$

As you can see from this pattern, the next difference needs to be 3, which makes the first answer 7. The next difference is −7, which makes the second answer 0.

**280.** In 15 years. There are several ways to solve this puzzle, one of which uses a chart comparing their movements. It helps to realize that the correct answer must involve whole-number (not fractional) revolutions.

| $y$ (3 years) | $x$ (5 years) |
|---|---|
| 3 years = 1 revolution | ⅗ revolution |
| 6 years = 2 revolutions | 1⅕ revolutions |
| 9 years = 3 revolutions | 1⅘ revolutions |
| 12 years = 4 revolutions | 2⅖ revolutions |
| 15 years = 5 revolutions | 3 revolutions |

**281.** Separating the men from the boys

**282.** 40. Here's one way to figure this out: there are 16 houses between number 12 and number 29. Since half of those have to be on each side, there are 8 more houses on each side. This makes the last home on one side house number 20, and there must be 20 more homes going back up the street, which makes a total of 40.

**283.** Alex is the second oldest. Their ages are:

Alicia: 30 years old
Alex: 25 years old
Amy: 5 years old

**284.** 24 miles per hour. Let's say Maria went 60 miles up and 60 miles back. It would then take her three hours up and two hours to get back. Five hours to go 120 miles is $^{120}/_5$ = 24 miles per hour.

**285.** C. This is the only figure that has both concave and convex features. The other figures have one or the other only.

**286.** 45 miles. Let $x$ be the distance from the beginning point to the turnaround point, and let $y$ be the time it takes to go downstream.

Downstream:     $\dfrac{x \text{ mi}}{30 \text{ mph}} = y$     (1)

Upstream:     $\dfrac{x \text{ mi}}{10 \text{ mph}} = y + 3$

$\dfrac{x}{10} - 3 = y$     (2)

Setting Eq. (1) equal to Eq. (2) gives

$$\frac{x}{30} = \frac{x}{10} - 3$$

$$x = 3x - 90$$

$$2x = 90$$

$$x = 45 \text{ miles}$$

**287.** $1\frac{7}{8}$ hours. In one hour, the first pipe fills half the pool, the second pipe fills $\frac{1}{5}$, and the third pipe empties $\frac{1}{6}$ of the pool. That is, in one hour the pool fills:

$$\frac{1}{2} + \frac{1}{5} - \frac{1}{6} = \frac{15}{30} + \frac{6}{30} - \frac{5}{30}$$
$$= \frac{16}{30}$$
$$= \frac{8}{15}$$

For the whole pool to fill, then, it takes $\frac{15}{8} = 1\frac{7}{8}$ hours.

**288.** TRIGONOMETRY

**289.** 7 in the second column, and 5 in the last column. If you delete the boxes and move the numbers together, you have a simple addition problem:

$$
\begin{array}{r}
16367 \\
+27198 \\
\hline
43565
\end{array}
$$

**290.** Here are the ones we found. Did you find others?

| | | | |
|---|---|---|---|
| math | thrice | timer | heat |
| rich | rice | crime | eat |
| chime | mice | crate | cheat |
| chimera | metric | cream | came |
| rat | time | ream | tame |
| cat | rime | treat | hater |
| hat | cite | threat | rate |
| mat | rite | tire | ate |
| tic | hate | mire | tea |
| mirth | mate | hire | team |
| chair | matte | it | mart |
| hair | act | teach | art |
| mare | tact | reach | cart |
| hare | them | meat | heart |

**291.** There are five sides to a pentagon.

**292.** Counterculture revolution

**293.** Greater. Let $x$ be the number of southpaws that are pitchers, $y$ be the number of all southpaws, $p$ be the number of all pitchers, and $q$ be the number of all ballplayers. Then we have

$$\frac{x}{p} > \frac{y}{q} \text{ or } xq > yp \text{ or } \frac{x}{y} > \frac{p}{q}$$

**294.** 6. Starting at the left, each group of three numbers adds up to 19.

**295.** –8. Above the line, either figure, circle or square, is worth +2 points apiece. Below the line, either figure is worth –2 points apiece. It makes no difference whether it is the circle or the square that comes first.

**296.** Standing at the end of the line

**297.** Here is one way:

**298.** Root canal

**299.** Hg

**300.** Remove the vertical match in the plus sign and place it next to the match sticks at the beginning of the equation

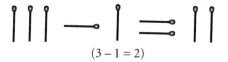

$$(3 - 1 = 2)$$

**301.** Here's one way:

TREAT
TREAD
BREAD
BREED
BLEED
BLEND
BLOND

**302.** FIRECRACKER

**303.** Tailgate party

**304.** 45. When ⅓ left, ⅔ of the people remained. When ⅖ left, ⅗ of ⅔ remained. When ⅔ of the remaining people left, ⅗ of ⅔ of ⅓ (or ⁶⁄₄₅) of the people remained. Since there were 6 people remaining, there were originally 45 people.

**305.** The letter e.

**306.** Seven

**307.** 44

**308.** It's hip to be square

**309.** Queen, queen, king, king, queen, king, queen, king

**310.**

| | | |
|---|---|---|
| Daffodils | Smiths | 1st Street |
| Roses | Johnsons | 2nd Street |
| Violets | Parks | 3rd Street |
| Begonias | Rosens | 4th Street |
| Peonies | Morgans | 5th Street |

**311.** The missing number is 127. Starting with (7, 8), the difference between each enclosed pair of numbers is: $1^3, 2^3, 3^3, 4^3, 5^3, 6^3$.

$$6^3 = 216$$
$$343 - 216 = 127$$

**312.** There are 14 days in a fortnight.

**313.** Male bonding

**314.** He who laughs last laughs best, or so they say.

**315.** PARALLEL

**316.** Here's one solution:

> PEST
> PAST
> PASS
> BASS
> BATS

**317.** Same time next year

**318.** There are 31 bounded areas that are not further subdivided. One way to approach this puzzle is to look for a pattern: two circles have three bounded areas; three circles have seven; four circles have 13. Five circles would then have 21 bounded areas. The pattern is increasing 4, 6, 8, 10, 12…so six circles would have 21 + 10 or 31 bounded areas.

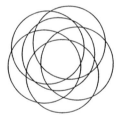

**319.** False. Some *zers* <u>may be</u> *wols*, but there is nothing to support the conclusion that some *zers* are definitely *wols*.

**320.** It equals 25. Compare the two equations in the question:

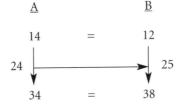

| A | | B |
|---|---|---|
| 14 | = | 12 |

24 → 25

| 34 | = | 38 |

The midpoint of column A is 24; the midpoint of column B is 25.

**321.** Here's one: POTPOURRI. What are some others?

**322.** A star in the making

**323.** Open forum

**324.** Figure 5 is the only one that doesn't include a square in its design.

**325.** False. Even if the premise were true, it does not automatically follow that only the most brilliant minds will succeed. The conclusion is too open-ended. Who determines what represents brilliance? Is it simply a matter of intelligence tests, or are there other considerations? Who chooses the criteria? Who decides what success is? Many questions need to be answered before this argument can be considered valid.

**326.** Piece of cake

**327.** 13:71

Glass 1 is $\frac{1}{6}$ dye + $\frac{5}{6}$ water

Glass 2 is $\frac{1}{7}$ dye + $\frac{6}{7}$ water

Total dye in mixture =

$$\frac{1}{6} + \frac{1}{7} = \frac{13}{42}$$

Total water in mixture =

$$\frac{5}{6} + \frac{6}{7} = \frac{35}{42} + \frac{36}{42} = \frac{71}{42}$$

$\frac{13}{42}$ parts blue dye and $\frac{71}{42}$ parts water

**328.** CALCULATOR

**329.** −9. The second number in each box is 1 less than the cube of the first number.

**330.** A friend in need is a friend indeed

**331.** 7. The decimal representation of the fraction $^1/_{29}$ is .0344827. On some calculators, the digit 7 in that number is rounded off to 8.

**332.** 35. Bottom level, 18; second level, 12; third level, 4; top level, 1.

**333.**     Harry—June—Red
John—Alice—Blue
Brad—Nancy—White
Steve—Sara—Yellow

**334.** A day at a time

**335.** Each is a different word when spelled backward. Such words are called recurrent palindromes.

**336.**

In each row, the pattern of lines in the second column has been subtracted from the pattern in the first column to produce the figure in the third column.

**337.** Meeting of the minds

**338.** I am 24 years old and my sister is 4 years old. Here's one way to derive the answer:

Let $x$ = my sister's age, and $y$ = my age.

$y = 6x$  AND  $y + 1 = 5(x + 1) = 5x + 5$

subtracting 1 from both sides of the second equation $y = 5x + 4$

substituting this for y in the first equation $5x + 4 = 6x$

subtacting $5x$ from both sides of the resulting equation $x = 4$

substituting this result back into the first equation $y = 6 \times 4 = 24$

**339.** The words on the left have three consecutive letters of the alphabet in reverse order: <u>fed</u>eral, <u>pon</u>d, <u>rut</u>s. The words on the right have three consecutive letters of the alphabet in the correct order: <u>def</u>y, <u>hij</u>ack, cal<u>mn</u>ess.

**340.** She put all nine scoops of ice cream into a blender and made milk shakes.

**341.** Spiral notebook

**342.** Pick up one penny on the first move and you can't be beat. Did you find any other winning move?

**343.** There are 24 karats in pure gold.

**344.** Here's how the words and the patterns are related: The letter L is used with the patterns whose individual components are separated. T goes with the patterns whose components are interlocked. R corresponds to three components and W to two. I goes with the snowman patterns, and U goes with the circles. For the two interlocked snowmen, the new word is TIW. The last pattern looks like this:

**345.** Twelve. Since 15 dealers have fewer than 5 cards, those 15 are eliminated from consideration. Three have more than 7 cards, so they are eliminated. Eleven have more than 6 cards, which means all 11 must have exactly 7 cards. This totals to 15 + 3 + 11 = 29 dealers, leaving one dealer we haven't mentioned (tricky, huh?), who must have exactly 5 or 6 cards.

**346.** T, for thirteen. These are the first letters of the odd numbers, in ascending order, beginning with one.

**347.**

```
    982
    982
    982
 +7,982
 10,928
```

**348.** 2,913. There are a couple of ways to solve this puzzle. The first way builds the series by summing squares and cubes in an interesting way:

$$1^2 + 2^3 = 1 + 8 = 9$$
$$3^2 + 4^3 = 9 + 64 = 73$$
$$5^2 + 6^3 = 25 + 168 = 241$$
$$7^2 + 8^3 = 49 + 512 = 561$$
$$9^2 + 10^3 = 81 + 1,000 = 1,081$$
$$11^2 + 12^3 = 121 + 1,728 = 1,849$$
$$13^2 + 14^3 = 169 + 2,744 = 2,913$$

Another approach involves taking the "difference of the differences." From the pattern continuing 48s that results, you can build back up the answer of 2913:

| 9 | | 73 | | 241 | | 561 | | 1,081 | | 1,849 | | 2,913 |
|---|---|----|---|-----|---|-----|---|-------|---|-------|---|-------|
| | 64 | | 168 | | 320 | | 520 | | 768 | | | | 1,064 |
| | | 104 | | 152 | | 200 | | 248 | | | | | 296 |
| | | | 48 | | 48 | | 48 | | | | | | 48 |

**349.** Border guards

**350.** 1 mph. Bob was rowing at a constant rate in relation to the water, and it took him 8 hours to travel 24 miles. At the point where he lost his hat, he had been rowing for 6 miles, or 2 hours. To meet Bob where he began his journey, the hat had to travel downstream 6 miles. Bob didn't reach the hat until after he had rowed the remaining 18 miles, or for 6 more hours. Thus, it took the hat 6 hours to travel 6 miles, carried by the stream at a velocity of 1 mph.

$$6 \text{ miles}/6 \text{ hours} = 1 \text{ mph}$$

**351.** Here's one way to solve the zookeeper's problem:

Put nine snakes in each of three cages, and put those three cages within a fourth, larger cage, in case any snakes escape from one of the smaller cages.

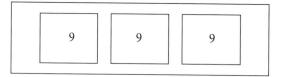

**352.** 225 squares on a Scrabble board

**353.** 4

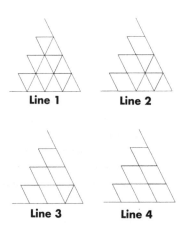

**354.** *The Rise and Fall of the Roman Empire*

**355.** 90 seconds. In 1 minute the man can walk 1 length in the forward direction, but only one-third of a length in the backward direction. Factoring out the effects of the walkway's speed, we find that in 1 minute the man can walk

$$\frac{1 + \frac{1}{3}}{2}$$

or $\frac{2}{3}$ of a length in one minute.

This means that the man can walk one length of the stationary walkway in $\frac{3}{2} \times 60 = 90$ seconds.

**356.** Chain link fencing

**357.** Here's a start:

| | | |
|---|---|---|
| raze | daze | red |
| race | read | dear |
| razed | dare | ace |
| raced | cared | aced |
| zed | care | are |

**358.** T. These are capital letters, beginning with A, that contain straight lines only.

**359.** C. All of the patterns contain a figure similar to a capital F except pattern C, which has a backwards F.

**360.** $(9!^{9!^{9!}})!$

**361.** FUTURISTIC

**362.** 195. The lowest common denominator of 3, 5, and 13 is 3 × 5 × 13 = 195.

**363.** Placed under arrest

**364.** Here's one version:

> PULL
> PILL
> PILE
> BILE
> BITE

**365.** 21. Starting with the two outside numbers and moving toward the middle, each pair adds up to 60.

**366.** Each is a 5-letter word that becomes a 4-letter word when its first letter is removed.

**367.** Conundrum

**368.** SYNONYM

**369.** Harvard would beat Montana by 16 points. Here's how to find the answer:

Maine beat BYU by 32 – 3 = 29 points, and Ohio State beat BYU by 10 – 7 = 3 points.

So if Maine were to play Ohio State, they would win by 29 – 3 = 26 points. Notre Dame beat Ohio State by 14 – 10 = 4 points and, since Maine would beat Ohio State by 26, they would beat Notre Dame by 26 – 4 = 22 points.

Montana beat Notre Dame by 27 − 13 = 14 points and, since Maine would beat Notre Dame by 22, they would beat Montana by 22 − 14 = 8 points.

But Connecticut beat Maine by 28 − 24 = 4 points, so, because Maine would beat Montana by 8, Connecticut would beat Montana by 4 + 8 = 12 points.

New Hampshire beat Connecticut by 24 − 21 = 3, so, because Connecticut would beat Montana by 12, New Hampshire would beat Montana by 3 + 12 + 15 points.

Finally, Harvard beat New Hampshire by 1 point, so, because New Hampshire would beat Montana by 15, Harvard would beat Montana by 1 + 15 = 16 points.

**370.** You're as young as you feel. To decode, find the code letter in the bottom row and translate it into the corresponding letter in the top row:

A B C D E F G H I  J K L M N O P Q R S  T U V W X Y Z

L M N O P Q R  S T U V W X Y Z A B C D E F G H I  J K

**371.** There were 20 nickels and 20 dimes. To solve this, set up the following equations, where n = nickels and d = dimes:

$$n = d$$
$$.05n + .10d = 3.00$$
$$.05n + .10n = 3.00$$
$$.15n = 3.00$$
$$n = 20$$

**372.** Lowering the boom

**373.** $x = 5$, $y = 6$, and $z = 4$, so the sum is 15. The variable $x$ can be either 0 or 5. It must be 5 because there is no number that ends in 0 when multiplied by 7 ($y \times 7$, resulting in $x$ in the ones place). Therefore, a 3 is carried over to the $y$. Since $x$ is 5, $y$ must be 6 because $7 \times 6 = 42$. Add the 3 that was carried over and you get 45. Therefore, $z$ is 4.

**374.** The answer is 96. Set up the following equations:

$$\tfrac{1}{2} \times \tfrac{2}{3} \times \tfrac{3}{5} = \tfrac{6}{30} = \tfrac{1}{5}$$
$$\tfrac{1}{5} \times 240 = 48$$
$$48 \div \tfrac{1}{2} = 96$$

**375.** It might be helpful to set up a grid as follows:

|        | Basketball | Football | Baseball |
|--------|------------|----------|----------|
| Alex   | x          |          | o        |
| Ryan   | o          |          |          |
| Steven | x          | o        | x        |

We can see that Ryan must like basketball since neither Alex nor Steven does. Steven does not like basketball or baseball, so he must like football, leaving Alex liking baseball.

**376.** Seven zips have the weight of 1 wob. The problem can be set up as follows:

$$26z = 4c + 2w$$
$$8z + 2c = 2w$$

Rearranging, we get

$$(1)\ 26z = 4c + 2w$$
$$(2)\ 8z = -2c + 2w$$

Multiply equation (2) by 2 so that the $c$ factor drops out, and combine the two equations:

$$
\begin{array}{rl}
26z = & 4c + 2w \\
16z = & -4c + 4w \\
\hline
42z = & 6w \\
7z = & w
\end{array}
$$

**377.** Look before you leap

**378.** The missing number is 10. The numbers in each circle add up to 50.

**379.** It's the right thing to do

**380.** The next letter is P. The differences between letters form the pattern 1, 2, 1, 2, 1, 2…

**381.** The answer is "three words."

**382.** The chances are 1 in 3. Here are all the possible draws (C1 = first cherry gumdrop, C2 = second cherry gumdrop, O = orange gumdrop):

| First draw | Second draw |
|------------|-------------|
| C1 | C2 |
| C1 | O |
| C2 | C1 |
| C2 | O |
| O | C1 |
| O | C2 |

Among the six possible draws, O appears twice in the second draw column; thus the chances are 2 in 6, or 1 in 3.

**383.** Figure 4 is the only one that doesn't contain a triangle.

**384.** The lesser of two evils.

**385.** It is impossible to average 60 miles per hour for this trip. At 30 miles per hour, the car would travel one mile in two minutes; at 60 miles per hour, the car would travel two miles in two minutes. So, in order to average 60 mph, the entire trip of two miles would have to be completed in two minutes. But the driver has already used two minutes going from point A to point B; there's not time left to get from point B to point C.

**386.** Here's one way to solve the puzzle:

$$TOOK$$
$$BOOK$$
$$BOON$$
$$BORN$$
$$BURN$$

**387.** 6.25 percent. Remember, length × width = area. Let $l$ = length and $w$ = width. Then

$$l + .25l = 1.25l$$
$$w - .25w = .75w$$
$$1.25l \times .75w = 93.75$$

Finally,

$$100 - 93.75 = 6.25$$

**388.** Five.

**389.** The "R" goes above the line. The letters above the line are closed with a space inside them.

**390.** Time slips into the future

**391.** Let $x$ = the fraction. Then:

$$(3 \times \tfrac{1}{4}x) \times x = \tfrac{1}{12}$$
$$\tfrac{3}{4}x^2 = \tfrac{1}{12}$$
$$x^2 = \tfrac{1}{9}$$
$$x = \tfrac{1}{3}$$

**392.** There are 100 years in a century.

**393.** Two miles. They are actually eating up the distance at 120 miles per hour (50 + 70):

$$\frac{120 \text{ miles}}{60 \text{ minutes}} = \text{two miles in one minute}$$

**394.** Pocket full of money

**395.** They can be combined in 12 different ways.

**396.** $^1\!/_{24}$

$$\frac{3}{32} - \frac{1}{16} = \frac{1}{32}$$

$$4 \times (\frac{1}{3} \times \frac{1}{32}) = \frac{4}{96} \ \text{ or } \ \frac{1}{24}$$

**397.** The letters "mot" will create the words "mother," "motion," "motor," "motif," and "motto."

**398.** The ratio is 1 to 2. One way to solve this problem is to set up an equation in which $x$ equals the amount of $48 chemical used and $y$ equals the amount of $36 chemical used:

$$\begin{aligned}
48x + 36y &= 40(x + y) \\
48x + 36y &= 40x + 40y \\
8x &= 4y \\
\frac{x}{y} &= \frac{1}{2}
\end{aligned}$$

**399.** The answer is (e). Remember, $x$ may be a negative number.

**400.** $.1 \times .9 \times .8 = .072$

**401.** Line dance

**402.** Traffic jam

**403.** He would have 20 pleezorns. Count the letters in each name and multiply by 2.

**404.** The ratio is 1 to 2. It might help to set up the problem as follows:

$$\frac{5x}{4y} = \frac{7}{8}$$

$$40x = 28y$$

$$10x = 7y$$

Thus, $10x$ to $7y$ is a 1-to-1 relationship. We are asked for the ratio of $10x$ to $14y$; since $14 = 7 \times 2$, we can see that it is a 1-to-2 relationship.

**405.** There are 31 triangles.

**406.** Don't count your chickens before they hatch.

**407.** Here are 20 four-letter words

| | | |
|---|---|---|
| twin | wine | lint |
| kiln | kilt | lent |
| wink | wilt | like |
| link | welt | kine |
| tine | tile | lien |
| newt | kite | line |
| went | wile | |

**408.** The answer is 13,222.

$$
\begin{array}{r}
12,000 \\
+1,222 \\
\hline
13,222
\end{array}
$$

**409.** Three-ring circus

**410.** JJ. The letters are the initial letters of pairs of month names, starting with October-November.

**411.** Forward thinking

**412.** Draw a line as follows and you'll see the answer, June:

**413.** Double-decker sandwich

**414.** In the first case, $2^{67}$ is larger. In the second case, they are equal.

**415.** Microorganism

**416.** There is one wheel on a unicycle.

**417.** Fifteen angles of less than 90 degrees can be formed.

**418.** Here they are:

$$\frac{1}{2} = \frac{6{,}729}{13{,}458}$$

$$\frac{1}{3} = \frac{5{,}832}{17{,}496}$$

$$\frac{1}{4} = \frac{4{,}392}{17{,}568}$$

$$\frac{1}{5} = \frac{2,769}{13,845}$$

$$\frac{1}{6} = \frac{2,943}{17,658}$$

$$\frac{1}{7} = \frac{2,394}{16,758}$$

$$\frac{1}{8} = \frac{3,187}{25,496}$$

$$\frac{1}{9} = \frac{6,381}{57,429}$$

**419.** i before e except after c

**420.** The missing numbers are 18 and 5, respectively. There are actually two separate series of numbers in this puzzle. Look at every other number, beginning first with 8 and then with 15.

**421.** Yes. A number is divisible by 8 if its last three digits are divisible by 8. Examples: 6,240; 9,184; 15,536.

**422.** The value of **z** must be 9 in all cases.

**423.** The value of **x** is 1. The variable **y** can have any of a number of values, but **x** must always equal 1 and **z** must always equal 9.

**424.** Doorbell. All the rest have handles.

**425.** You would write it 17 times. Don't forget that there are two 4s in 44!

**426.** Figure C is the only figure without a straight line.

**427.** For these three numbers, 455 is the lowest common denominator. The least number of pieces of candy is 455.

**428.** The answer is $^{10}/_{33}$. The problem can be solved as follows:

$$\cfrac{1}{3+\cfrac{1}{3\frac{1}{3}}} = \cfrac{1}{3+\cfrac{1}{\frac{10}{3}}} = \cfrac{1}{3+\frac{3}{10}} = \cfrac{1}{\frac{33}{10}} = \frac{10}{33}$$

**429.** Right cross followed by an uppercut.

**430.** 107 percent of 300 is greater. Because 107 percent is equivalent to 1.07, we have

$$1.07 \times 300 = 321$$
$$.50 \times 600 = 300$$

**431.** You would receive 221 silver pieces. If you were to exchange your kooklas only for gold, it would require $40 \times 7$ or 280 pieces. But there are only 161 gold pieces, leaving you 119 gold pieces short. The value of silver coins to gold coins is in the ratio of 13 to 7:

$$\frac{13}{7} = \frac{x}{119}$$
$$7x = 1,547$$
$$x = 221$$

**432.** Fill in the blanks.

**433.** Here's one way:

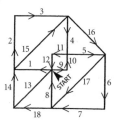

**434.**

| 1 | 8 | 13 | 12 |
|---|---|----|----|
| 14 | 11 | 2 | 7 |
| 4 | 5 | 16 | 9 |
| 15 | 10 | 3 | 6 |

**435.** The missing number is 35. The second number in each box is the square of the first number minus 1.

**436.** There are 720 possible arrangements. Use the following equation to solve the problem (this is called factorial notation):

$$6! = 6 \times 5 \times 4 \times 3 \times 2 \times 1 = 720$$

**437.** Hole in one

**438.** The number 9 goes below the line and the number 10 goes above it—the numbers 1, 2, 6, and 10 are all spelled with three letters; the rest have four or more.

**439.** Algebra

**440.** Your eyes are bigger than your stomach

**441.** Here are two examples:
1. When giving yes and no answers, a person who tells a lie about a lie is telling the truth.
2. Imagine a child rolling his wagon backward down a hill. If you were to film this and run the film backward, you would see the wagon going forward up the hill.

**442.**
$$8 \frac{88}{88}$$

**443.** Elbow grease

**444.** There are 24 cubes.

**445.** $x$, $y$, and $z$ = 8, 12, and 60 pounds, respectively. Starting with the 8 ft. section.

$$8 \text{ ft.} \times 10 \text{ lbs.} = 80 \text{ ft.-lbs.}$$

To balance, the bottom left part of the mobile must also equal 80 ft.-lbs., so its total weight must be 20 lbs. (4 ft. × 20 lbs. = 80 ft.-lbs.) Therefore,

$$x + y = 20$$
$$\text{and}$$
$$6x = 4y.$$
$$\text{So, } y = 20 - x$$
$$\text{and substituting,}$$

$$6x = 4(20 - x)$$
$$6x = 80 - 4x$$
$$10x = 80$$
$$x = 8$$

and therefore,

$$y = 12.$$

Adding the total weights of the left side, we have

$$120 + 10 + 8 + 12 = 150 \text{ lbs.}$$
$$150 \text{ lbs.} \times 4 \text{ ft.} = 600 \text{ ft.-lbs.}$$

Therefore, the right side must also be 600 ft.-lbs.:

$$10 \text{ ft.} \times z \text{ lbs.} = 600 \text{ ft.-lbs.}$$

$$z = 60$$

**446.** They say at least 100 words can be made from "Thanksgiving." How many can you find?

**447.** It is $7/9$. The problem can be approached as follows:

$$1/10 \div 1/2 \div 1/5 = 1/10 \times 2 \times 5 = 1$$

$$1 \times 7/9 = 7/9$$

**448.** All answers are divisible by three.

**449.** The square is 6 feet by 6 feet. To solve this problem, let $x$ represent each side of the square. Then

$$4x = x^2 \times \frac{2}{3}$$
$$12x = 2x^2$$
$$6x = x^2$$
$$x = 6$$

**450.** Shrinking violets

**451.** Calm before the storm

**452.**

>                    MOOD
>                    MOON
>                    MORN
>                    BORN
>                    BARN

**453.** 2 in 9. Because each die has 6 faces, there are 6 × 6 or 36 possible combinations of numbers. Of these, 6 combinations result in a 7:

>                    6 and 1
>                    1 and 6
>                    5 and 2
>                    2 and 5
>                    4 and 3
>                    3 and 4

And 2 combinations result in an 11:

>                    5 and 6
>                    6 and 5

thus the chances are 8 in 36, or 2 in 9.

**454.** T = 15. Since A = 2, we can substitute A into the first four equations to come up with the following:

$$(1) \qquad 2 + B = H$$
$$(2) \qquad H + P = T$$
$$(3) \qquad T + 2 = F$$
$$(4) \quad B + P + F = 30$$

Now substitute equation (1) into equation (2):

$$(2 + B) + P = T$$

Rearranging, we get

$$B + P = T - 2$$

Substitute this into equation (4):

$$(T - 2) + F = 30$$

Finally, substitute equation (3) into equation (4) and solve for T:

$$(T - 2) + (T + 2) = 30$$
$$2T = 30$$
$$T = 15$$

**455.** An onion costs 7 cents. Set up the equations, with $x$ as potatoes and $y$ as onions:

$$5x + 6y = 1.22$$
$$6x + 5y = 1.31$$

Multiply the first equation by 6, the second one by 5:

$$30x + 36y = 7.32$$
$$30x + 25y = 6.55$$

Subtract the second equation from the first, and you have:

$$0x + 11y = .77$$
$$y = .07$$

**456.** Let's have $x$, $y$, and $z$ represent three types of candles.

$$x + y + z = 100$$

and

$$.50x + 5.50y + 9.50z = \$100$$

Multiply the first equation by $-.5$, and combine it with the second equation:

$$-.5x - .5y - .5z = -50$$
$$.5x + 5.5y + 9.5z = 100$$

$$5y + 9z = 50$$
$$5y = 50 - 9z$$
$$y = 10 - \frac{9}{5}z$$

Since we're dealing with whole numbers, $z$ must be a whole number and a multiple of 5. In this case $z$ can only equal 5. With any greater number, $y$ will become negative, so $z = 5$, $y = 1$, and thus $x$ must be 94. $(94 \times .50) + (1 \times 5.50) + (5 \times 9.50) = \$100$.

**457.** Rising tide

**458.** The missing number is zero. If you convert each fraction to twelfths, you get the following series:

$$\frac{5}{12} \qquad \frac{4}{12} \qquad \frac{3}{12} \qquad \frac{2}{12} \qquad \frac{1}{12} \qquad 0$$

**459.** Factors of the number 12 $(6 + 4 + 3 + 2 + 1)$ add up to 16.

**460.** It can be done as follows:

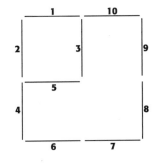

**461.** There are 206 bones in the human body.

**462.** 18. ¼ of ⅓ of ⅙ is ¹⁄₇₂; ¹⁄₇₂ of 432 is 6; and 6 divided by ⅓ is 18.

**463.** Multiplication tables

**464.** Fifty-six applicants have experience in selling both golf equipment and athletic shoes. Since 13 of the applicants have had no sales experience, we're dealing with 87 people who have some experience. Of the 87 applicants, 65 of them have sold golf equipment, which means that 22 of this group haven't sold golf equipment (87 – 65 = 22). Seventy-eight of the applicants have sold shoes, which means that 9 haven't (87 – 78 = 9). Therefore, we have 9 + 22 or 31 people who could not have sold both—thus, 87 – 31 = 56 people who *have* had experience in selling both.

**465.** Deep in thought

**466.** 110 square yards. An area 11 yards square measures 11 yards on each of four sides and therefore has a total of 121 square yards. An area of 11 square yards, if it were square, would be just under 3.32 yards on each side. The difference between the two, then, is found by subtracting 11 square yards from 121 square yards: 110 square yards.

**467.** Life

**468.** You are on time

**469.** 6009, 6119

**470.** Seven. These are the elements hydrogen, carbon, and nitrogen with their respective atomic numbers; seven is the atomic number for nitrogen.

**472.** Can't see the forest for the trees

**472.** They are 496 and 8,128. The next perfect number after that is 33,550,336!

**473.** There are 16 possibilities, each having a probability of $\frac{1}{16}$. There are 6 ways with exactly 2 tails, 4 ways with 3 tails, and 1 way with 4 tails. That's a total of 11 ways out of 16. The chances are 11 in 16.

| | |
|---|---|
| HHHH | TTTT |
| HTTT | THHH |
| HHHT | TTTH |
| HTHH | THTT |
| HHTH | TTHT |
| HHTT | TTHH |
| HTHT | THTH |
| HTTH | THHT |

**474.** A break in the action

**475.** Let a smile be your umbrella.

**476.** They are directly opposite each other 11 times.

**477.** It will take 1.2 hours.

The equation can be set up this way:

$$\frac{x}{3} + \frac{x}{2} = 1$$

Multiply by 6:

$$2x + 3x = 6$$
$$5x = 6$$
$$x = \frac{6}{5} = 1.2$$

**478.**

**479.** I am 19 years old and my sister is 9.
Let $x$ = my sister's age and $y$ = my age.

$$y = x + 10 \text{ and}$$
$$y + 1 = 2(x + 1)$$
$$y = 2x + 1$$

Substituting this result in our first equation, we have

$$2x + 1 = x + 10$$
$$x = 9$$

so

$$y = 19.$$

When my sister was 5, I was 3 times older than she was.

**480.** The missing letter is S. These are the first letters of the even numbers when spelled out, beginning with two.

**481.** Upside-down cake

**482.** Women are the better workers. Let's say that in one day, 10 men work at a rate of $x$ and 8 women work at a rate of $y$.

$$10x + 8y = \tfrac{1}{12} \text{ (one day), or } 120x + 96y = 1$$

Likewise in the second case:

$$8x + 12y = \tfrac{1}{10}, \text{ or } 80x + 120y = 1.$$

Therefore:

$$120x + 96y = 80x + 120y$$
$$5x = 3y$$

Thus, 3 women do the work of 5 men.

**483.** Sally Billingsley and Susie Jenkins are the real names. Because one of the first two statements had to be false, the third statement also had to be false.

**484.** The missing letter is N; the word is "sandwich."

**485.** 20 percent. Say there are 10 caramels. Since the number of caramels is 25 percent of the number of other candies, there must be 40 pieces of candy that aren't caramels. The total number of pieces of candy = 10 + 40 = 50, so $^{10}/_{50} = \frac{1}{5}$ = 20 percent.

**486.** Power surge

**487.** None. Instead, turn the puzzle upside-down and add:

$$
\begin{array}{r}
86 \\
91 \\
+68 \\
\hline
245
\end{array}
$$

**488.** Fender bender

**489.** Here's one way to solve the puzzle:

> ROAD
> ROAM
> ROOM
> LOOM
> LOOP

**490.** There are 106 elements in the periodic table.

**491.** Diagram E is the odd one out. The other four are symmetrical about both of their axes: if you turn them 90 degrees, they will look the same as in their original positions.

**492.** $9 \times 8 \times 7 \times 6 \times 5 \times 4 \times 3 \times 2 \times 1 = 362,880$ different seating arrangements. In mathematics, this is written "9!" and called "factorial 9."

**493.**

$$
\begin{aligned}
C &= 100 \\
D &= 500 \\
\overline{M} &= 1,000 \\
\overline{V} &= 5,000 \\
\overline{X} &= 10,000 \\
\overline{L} &= 50,000 \\
\overline{C} &= 100,000 \\
\overline{D} &= 500,000 \\
\overline{M} &= 1,000,000
\end{aligned}
$$

**494.** The chances are still 1 in 50.

**495.** The missing number is $\frac{1}{30}$. The series is constructed as follows:

$$12 = \frac{1}{2} \text{ of } 84$$
$$2 = \frac{1}{6} \text{ of } 12$$
$$\frac{2}{5} = \frac{1}{5} \text{ of } 2$$
$$\frac{1}{10} = \frac{1}{4} \text{ of } \frac{2}{5}$$
$$\frac{1}{30} = \frac{1}{3} \text{ of } \frac{1}{10}$$

**496.** Current affair

**497.** $96. Use the equation

$$\frac{1}{4}x - (\frac{3}{4} \times \frac{1}{4}x) = \$6$$
$$\frac{1}{4}x - \frac{3}{16}x = \$6$$

Multiply each side by 16:

$$4x - 3x = \$96$$
$$x = \$96$$

**498.** She is their aunt.

**499.** Central Intelligence Agency

**500.** "Lapy" means tree. From the first two phrases, "rota" must mean apple. From the third phrase, "mena" must mean large, leaving "lapy" to be tree.

**501.** Hologram

**502.** Guilty beyond a reasonable doubt

**503.** The numbers in each circle add up to 150, so the missing number is 23.

**504.** The missing number is 7. The numbers have a one-to-one correspondence with the letters of the alphabet, where A = 1, B = 2, C = 3, and so forth. The word spelled out is "mind-bending."

**505.** No time left on the clock

**506.** There are 180 degrees in a triangle.

**507.** Book

**508.** Four people can sit in five seats as follows:

$5 \times 4 \times 3 \times 2$, for a total of 120 different ways

**509.**

$34/650$ or $17/325$

$1/10$ less than $3/13$ is:

$30/130 - 13/130 = 17/130$

4 times $\frac{1}{10}$ of that number is:

$$4 \times \frac{1}{10} \times \frac{17}{130} = \frac{4}{10} \times \frac{17}{130}$$

$$= \frac{2}{5} \times \frac{17}{130}$$

$$= \frac{34}{650}$$

$$= \frac{17}{325}$$

**510.** The weight should be placed 10 feet from the fulcrum. To solve this, first calculate foot-pounds (a unit of work combining force and distance) on the left side:

$$(5 \text{ ft.} \times 8 \text{ lbs.}) + (10 \text{ ft.} \times 10 \text{ lbs.}) = 140 \text{ ft.-lbs.}$$

The right side must equal the left side:

$$x \text{ ft.} \times 14 \text{ lbs.} = 140 \text{ ft.-lbs.}$$

Solving for $x$, we get

$$x = \frac{140}{14} = 10$$

**511.** There are 19 squares.

**512.** Slim chance

**513.** The missing number is 6. Keep taking the differences between numbers (keeping in mind positive and negative differences) and you get:

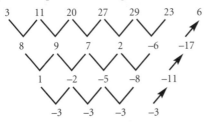

**514.** Transparent

**515.** POTS, SPOT, and OPTS. These are the only three remaining four-letter words that can be made by using the letters O, P, S, and T only once.

**516.** Knock on wood.

**517.**

BIKE
BITE
MITE
MATE
MATH

**518.** Dirty dozen

**519.** With players for each match through six rounds, $2^6$ or 64 players are entered.

**520.** Each layer would contain a number of balls equal to the square of the layer. In other words, layer 1 (the top layer) would have $1^2 = 1$ ball; layer 2 would have $2^2 = 4$ balls; layer 3 would have $3^2 = 9$ balls; and so on. The layers would stack up like this, for a total of 140 balls.

1
4
6
25
36
49
—
140

**521.** From left to right, the weights are 200 lbs., 120 lbs., 102 lbs., and 68 lbs.

First we find the two weights on the left. Their total weight (call it $a$) at a distance of 4 ft must balance 160 lbs. at a distance of 8 ft:

$$4a = 8 \times 160$$
$$a = 1,280 \div 4 = 320 \text{ lbs.}$$

Then $^5\!/\!_8$ of this weight at 3 ft must balance $^3\!/\!_8$ of this weight at 5 ft:

$$\frac{5}{8} \times 320 = 200 \text{ lbs. and } \frac{3}{8} \times 320 = 120 \text{ lbs.}$$

Next we find the two weights on the right. Their total weight (call it $b$) at a distance of 12 ft must balance $200 + 120 + 160 + 30 = 510$ lbs. at a distance of 4 ft:

$$12b = 4 \times 510$$
$$b = 2040 \div 12 = 170 \text{ lbs.}$$

Then $^6\!/\!_{10}$ of this weight at 4 ft must balance $^4\!/\!_{10}$ of this weight at 6 ft:

$$\frac{6}{10} \times 170 = 102 \text{ lbs. and } \frac{4}{10} \times 170 = 68 \text{ lbs.}$$

**522.** Five. Square 1 is the largest square and frames the whole figure. Then square 2 is placed in the lower right corner, and square 3 is placed in the upper left corner. (Square 2 and square 3 are the same size.) Square 4 is placed over square 3 in the upper-left corner, and square 5 is placed in the middle.

**523.** There are 24 letters in the Greek alphabet.

**524.** Close shave

**525.** The best approach to this problem is to find a common denominator of 2, 4, and 7 that is less than 30—that is 28. Then add up the calculated numbers of students:

> 2 students received a B
>
> $\frac{1}{4}$ of 28 = 7 students failed
>
> $\frac{1}{2}$ of 28 = 14 students received a D
>
> $\frac{1}{7}$ of 28 = 4 students received a C

totalling 27, which means only 1 student received an A.

# INDEX

*Note: Numbers represent the puzzle number.*

Age, 16, 60, 283, 338, 479
Algebra, 21, 36, 70, 78, 84, 88, 161, 237, 280, 355, 374, 414, 441, 487, 509
Alphametic puzzles, 194, 229, 254, 258, 347, 373, 422, 423, 454
Analogy, 14, 122, 212, 470
Analytical reasoning, 51, 195, 344
Angles, 417
Animals, 244, 351
Area, 466
Arrangements, 436, 492, 508

Balance puzzles, 49, 203, 445, 510, 521

Chance. *See* Probability
Circles, 318, 503
Clocks, 9, 102, 476
Code deciphering, 33, 37, 163, 177, 248, 370
Cryptograms, 105, 117, 180, 259, 406, 475, 516
Cubes, 73, 100, 167, 183, 192, 256, 272, 306, 307, 332, 444

Days of week, 57
Distance, 385, 393, 510

Division, 233, 340, 362, 374, 421, 427, 462

Electricity, 111
Equations, 1, 13, 220, 246, 320, 442, 454

Family relationships, 104, 150, 187, 216, 231, 278, 498
Foreign language, 82, 500
Fractions, 10, 22, 67, 77, 153, 165, 181, 193, 205, 211, 235, 274, 340, 374,
        391, 396, 418, 428, 447, 462, 497, 509, 525

Frame Game, 5, 11, 18, 20, 23, 28, 35, 40, 47, 52, 58, 63, 69, 71, 79, 81, 85,
        89, 91, 97, 103, 109, 112, 120, 124, 128, 131, 135, 138, 140,
        144, 151, 154, 159, 171, 174, 176, 179, 182, 184, 190, 200,
        204, 210, 213, 215, 218, 222, 230, 236, 240, 257, 262, 265,
        271, 273, 275, 281, 292, 296, 298, 303, 308, 313, 317, 322,
        323, 326, 330, 334, 337, 341, 349, 354, 356, 363, 372, 377,
        379, 384, 390, 394, 401, 402, 409, 411, 413, 419, 429, 432,
        437, 440, 443, 450, 451, 457, 463, 465, 468, 471, 474, 481,
        486, 488, 496, 499, 502, 505, 512, 518, 524

Geometry, 38, 95, 96, 247

Hidden phrase or title. See Frame Game

Intersections, 318

Letters, 93, 114, 162, 214, 241, 305, 346, 358, 380, 410, 412, 480, 484
Logic puzzles, 41, 142, 172, 185, 207, 251, 266, 309, 310, 319, 325, 333,
        342, 369, 371, 375, 403, 464, 482, 483, 519

"Magic square," 434
Matchsticks, 147, 300, 460

Math, 7, 30, 42, 48, 50, 72, 116, 158, 189, 217, 223, 244, 253, 260, 304,
        345, 360, 399, 430, 448, 455, 525. *See* also Algrebra and Geometry.
Measurement, 136
Missing numbers, 2, 6, 8, 12, 74, 76, 80, 98, 121, 132, 224, 289, 311, 329,
        331, 348, 504, 513
Mixtures, 26, 327, 398
Money, 75, 101, 277, 371, 431, 455, 456, 497

Numbers, 4, 29, 83, 90, 110, 196, 242, 378, 408, 418, 425, 438, 459, 469,
        472. *See* also Missing numbers
Number series, 10, 17, 94, 127, 134, 148, 152, 166, 169, 178, 186, 199,
        228, 255, 261, 268, 279, 294, 311, 331, 348, 365, 420, 435,
        458, 495, 504, 513

Palindrome, 141, 238
Percentages, 34, 65, 206, 219, 387, 400, 430, 485
Perfect numbers, 39
Periodic table, 299
Probability, 24, 45, 62, 92, 118, 157, 232, 382, 453, 473, 494
Pyramids, 520

Rate per hour, 43, 59, 284, 286, 287, 350, 385
Ratio/proportion, 46, 293, 398
Reassembly of discs, 31
Rectangle intersections, 156
Relationship, determining, 56, 61, 130, 191, 198, 201, 234, 252, 285, 324,
        329, 336, 339, 359, 366, 383, 389, 424, 426,
        435, 438, 480, 491, 495, 504. *See* also Family
        relationships
Roman numerals, 115, 202, 493

Sentence/phrase completion, 53, 66, 106, 129, 137, 146, 170, 208, 225, 249, 252, 291, 312, 343, 352, 392, 416, 461, 490, 506, 523
Series, figure, 250, 263
Series, letter, 54, 480
Series, numerical. *See* Number series
Squares, 87, 108, 197, 227, 297, 388, 395, 433, 449, 511, 522

Three dimensional objects, 267
Time, 9, 102, 145, 160, 270, 385, 477
Time-distance, 3, 43, 286, 385, 393
Travel routes, 44, 433
Triangles, 19, 74, 95, 123, 239, 353, 405
"Trickle-down" puzzles, 15, 68, 99, 133, 143, 175, 209, 301, 316, 364, 386, 452, 517

Unscramble puzzles, 25, 113, 139, 226, 269, 302, 314, 315, 361, 368, 415, 439, 501, 514

Volume, 73

Weight, 49, 264, 376, 445, 510, 521
Word creation, 32, 126, 243, 290, 321, 357, 397, 407, 446, 467, 515
Word find, 86, 188, 221, 288, 328, 367
Word unscramble, *See* Unscramble puzzles.
Words, 27, 55, 107, 119, 125, 149, 155, 173, 276, 339, 344, 381, 500, 507